BRILLIANT IDEAS TO GET BOYS WRITING

FOR AGES 9–11

Gillian Crombie

Andrew Brodie

First published 2009 by A&C Black Publishers Limited
36 Soho Square, London W1D 3QY
www.acblack.com

ISBN 978-1408-124-84-0
Author © Gillian Crombie 2009
Series Editor Julia Stanton
Design © Anita Ruddell 2009
Cover photographs © Shutterstock
Illustrations © Bridget Mackeith

Photo credits:
Shutterstock: RS 3: 'White water rafting on the rapids' /Simon Krzic; 'Haunted House' /Jill Battaglia; 'Pyramids Giza' /Sculpies; 'Beijing Olympics, August 10th' /Jonathan Larsen; RS 20: 'Boys and bikes' /Diana Mary Jorgenson; 'Boys playing at Whitehaven beach' /Christopher Meder; 'Boys sitting on the dock' /Sonya Etchison; 'Children playing in the street, Dehli, India' /Galina Mikhalishina; RS 53: 'Tiger Woods at World Championship' /photogolfer; 'Lewis Hamilton' /afaizal; 'David Beckham, LA Galaxy' /Brandon Parry; 'Usain Bolt' /Pete Niesen; 'Dr Edward 'Buzz' Aldrin' /Tim Pleasant; RS 58: 'Flood' /Marc van Vuren; 'London, June 25th 2008' /BEEE; 'White water rafting' /Jonathan Noden-Wilkinson.

Istock: RS 53: 'Charles Dickens' /Duncan Walker.

Every effort has been made to contact copyright holders of material reproduced in this book. Any omissions will be rectified in subsequent printings if notice is given to the publishers.

A CIP record for this publication is available from the British Library.

Printed in Great Britain by Martins the Printers, Berwick-Upon-Tweed

This book is produced using paper that is made from wood grown in managed, sustainable forests. It is natural, renewable and recyclable. The logging and manufacturing processes conform to the environmental regulations of the country of origin.

**To see our full range of titles
visit www.acblack.com**

Contents

Introduction

Brilliant Ideas to Get Boys Writing aims to provide positive strategies and practical resources for boys, in particular, as they develop their writing skills in the classroom. All children become better writers by engaging in the process of writing often, although research in the last ten years has shown that boys face particular difficulties and therefore require targeted help to attain their potential. As in all learning, teachers are key to this process and many of the strategies to improve writing are the same for boys and girls, such as creating an inviting and creative environment. However, there are other strategies, such as an emphasis on 'active learning' and 'talk' which are more important to the acquisition of skills by boys.

The strategies which help boys become enthusiastic and independent authors, writing for different purposes and audiences are:

★ Creating an inviting environment
★ Providing good literature and text models
★ Planning for and understanding the writing process
★ Giving real and relevant reasons for (boys) writing
★ Creating active learning strategies, including talk and drama
★ The inclusion of visual media
★ The use of ICT
★ Planning meaningful cross-curricular activities
★ Using assessment and reflection

These strategies underpin all the activities and resources in this book. The activities are easy to follow and the instruction text has been kept to a minimum to make them less daunting for boys. All the activity and resource sheets can be used on their own or alongside other literacy schemes that are already established in your school. Throughout the book you will find lots of references to good literacy practices, such as shared reading and writing, adult scribing, demonstration, supported composition, in addition to the specific strategies to develop writing independence. Boys will develop and gain greater success and confidence in an atmosphere of support and encouragement. Praise from a caring adult can be the best reward for their efforts. The activities in this book will provide many opportunities for them to enjoy success and build confidence which, in turn, will develop a positive attitude towards writing and a resulting increase in self-esteem.

The writing process

The writing process is made up of specific steps. These are the steps used by all writers although, depending on the writing purpose and audience, some of them may be short-circuited. The units in *Brilliant Ideas to Get Boys Writing* develop these steps, giving emphasis to different features as the units progress.

The steps are:
★ **Pre-writing**
   Features talk and active learning strategies to gather thoughts and ideas, individually or in groups. Stage to define the purpose of the writing and the audience for the finished text.

★ **Making notes and drafting**
   Includes making notes of ideas and thoughts, discussing them and altering and adding to them. Stage to make first attempt at writing task and checking purpose and text type.

★ **Revising and polishing**
   The writer or writers improve their text, individually or in collaboration with others – altering and adding language features and improving vocabulary and text organisation.

★ **Editing and proofreading**
   Writers can check the language mechanics of their own text or have others do it for them.

★ **Reading and publishing**
   Sharing of text with audience, through a variety of media.

Brilliant strategies

Create an inviting environment
★ Have high expectations of boys
★ Engage and motivate reluctant boys
★ Promote confidence and creativity
★ Reflect boys' interests

Provide good literature and text models
★ Have available a varied mix of books which appeal to boys and reflect personal interests
★ Provide emotionally powerful texts and varied text types, including visual texts
★ Include literature with appropriate role models
★ Include popular and 'out of school' cultural models

Plan for and understanding the writing process
★ Plan brisk and structured lessons with clearly stated objectives
★ Include varied activities, building an understanding of the process
★ Demonstrate modelling of texts
★ Provide opportunities for paired and collaborative tasks
★ Use plenty of writing frames to provide structure, modify to suit tasks

Give real and relevant reasons for (boys) writing
★ Create a writing habit, a classroom focus, across subjects
★ Give choices in topic settings, particularly narrative
★ Use relevant topics and interests – boys respond well to real-world themes
★ Include an element of competition and allow boys to challenge themselves

Plan meaningful cross-curricular activities
★ Plan to introduce content and tasks from other subjects
★ Identify and use genres and text types associated with particular subjects
★ Plan writing tasks in specific subject areas to give boys a sense of real-world purpose

Create active learning strategies
★ Boys show a preference for active learning – provide opportunities throughout lessons
★ Use talk often – it helps boys in the formulation and articulation of ideas
★ Explicitly discuss models of writing and explore how writer's write
★ Use dramatic strategies, help develop understanding and expression

Include visual media
★ Boys respond to opportunities to work with visual media – cartoons, television, video etc.
★ Visual media as a starting point can help boys develop literacy and move to written text types
★ Use visual 'graphic organisers' to help structure text planning
★ Use visual texts to convey meaning and support written text types

Make use of ICT
★ Use multi-media text to stimulate discussion and ideas
★ ICT supports active and interactive task development and outcomes
★ Use ICT at all stages of the writing process
★ Use presentation software to increase boys' confidence

Use assessment and reflection
★ Set clear targets and link assessment to them
★ Give regular feedback, including individual progress
★ Use self-assessment and partner/peer review to encourage discussion of learning
★ Challenge boys to extend their writing

Worth reading
★ *Me Read? No Way!* A practical guide to improving boys' literacy skills – Ontario Education
★ *Improving boys' writing through visual literacy and drama* – Developed by Lancashire Literacy Team
★ *Literature search on improving boys' writing* – Caroline Daly, OFSTED

Using this book

For teachers:

Purpose, structure, language and visual features of text type.

Examples of 'forms' within the text type, or exemplars of the text type.

Suggestions for cross-curricular opportunities.

ARGUMENT

Purpose	to argue a case for or against an opinion, using evidence to support it
Structure	opening statement of opinion or point of view; arguments in support of the opinion, from strongest to weakest argument; facts in support of the opinion; conclusion with reinforcement of opinion and sometimes a recommendation
Language features	action verbs; emotive words and phrases; present tense; technical terms and specialist language; time and cause/effect connectives; may include quotes
Visual features	photographs; illustrations; charts and graphs
Examples	letters; newspaper and magazine editorials and articles; leaflets and posters; radio and television editorials and programmes

Cross-curricular suggestions

Geography
★ Children argue a case for the preservation of an area of natural beauty or geographic importance which is under threat.

PSHE
★ Children present an argument for the merits of recycling glass, paper and aluminium.

History
★ Children argue the case for and against some of the great historical debates, such as Richard III killed the 'princes in the tower' or those involved in the opening of King Tutankhamen's tomb were cursed and they all died early.

Challenges, opportunities, further activities to extend the unit.

Notes for each activity, with emphasis on strategies to support boys' engagement and learning.

Activity and talk-based ideas, which support boys learning, for getting started.

Links to numerous Resource Sheets and General Reference support materials available on the CD.

Suggestions for reflection and feedback opportunities.

TEACHER'S NOTES

Use the **Challenge Cards** (Resource Sheet 61) to extend the unit.

Activity Sheet 1
Begin the session by asking children how they might argue for something e.g. more computer time in the classroom. Ask them to discuss it with a partner, and then write their points on the board. Were all the points in favour of the opinion, or were there for and against? Tell children that when presenting an argument in favour of an opinion or point of view it is useful to have considered the other point of view, so that you can counter it. Together write some issues on the board such as 'Is having a school uniform a good thing? Should the school have a garden to grow vegetables? Should there be water coolers in every classroom? Give pairs of children a copy of the activity sheet and ask them to choose an issue. They plan an argument with their partner making notes of the arguments for and against. Soundings could be taken from other students and adults in the school, then the children decide on their own concluding point of view based on the evidence.

Activity Sheet 2
Discuss with children a range of community and global issues for them to discuss such as: Cars should not be allowed in the town centre. All zoos should be banned. Wearing of animal furs should be banned. Limited whale hunting should be allowed. Make a list on the board and ask children in groups to choose one of the issues to discuss further. Display the model text on Resource Sheet 60. Read the text together and add the structure and language features captions (at the bottom of the page) to it. Discuss the argument structure: Give an opening statement to introduce the topic; give arguments in support of your opinion; give your strongest point first; give evidence for your arguments; conclude with a statement and a call to action. Look for language features such as: action verbs; time connections; cause/effect connections emotive words and phrases; present tense; technical terms and specialist language. Ask the children to think of other words and phrases which could be used to improve the text. Give the activity sheet to pairs of children and ask them to choose one of the issues discussed earlier and make notes for their argument. Once they have researched and made their points they write a draft of their argument. Suggest that they swap drafts with someone and review each other's work. (Resource Sheet 30 can be used.) They make alterations to their draft using the 'Proofreading' General Sheet and write (or type) a polished version of their argument.

Activity Sheet 3
Explore with children a range of different graphic organisers they can use to martial the points for their arguments, i.e. a logic chain, a flow chart, a Venn diagram. Ask children to choose another issue, for instance: Tourism is a good thing. Schools should devote one afternoon per week to sport. A wind farm should not to be built near the school. Children should be made to study a Martial Art. Why we

should use more electric cars rather than diesel or petrol vehicles. Give children the activity sheet and ask them to research the arguments for and against their chosen issue. Ask them to look for evidence for each of their arguments, and to make a list of source material on the back of the sheet. When they have completed their sheets, put them into groups of four and ask two to take one side of the argument and two to take the other side. Give them five minutes to think about their own arguments, then ask them to role-play their arguments in a discussion. The discussions could be recorded, or some groups could be asked to role-play for the class. In a plenary, discuss the arguments used, and their effectiveness.

Activity Sheet 4
Discuss the issue of schools selling off their playing fields in order to make money. Ask for views and have an open discussion of the arguments for and against this. Write up pros and cons and appropriate vocabulary on the board. Give the activity sheet to pairs of children and ask them to discuss and then lay out their arguments against (or for) this proposal for their school. The sheet can be used to make notes. When they have made their notes and drafted their arguments they either use their arguments to write a letter which could be sent to the council (using the argument structure in their letter) or create a PowerPoint presentation which could be shown to the school council. Remind them that it will help their argument if they can provide a sensible alternative solution and that they should have a clear and achievable call to action.

Activity Sheet 5
Give children the opportunity to listen to the arguments for and against an issue, either by listening to a radio debate, watching one on television or listening to a discussion by class members. Give them the activity sheet on which to make notes as they listen. Ask them to listen carefully as the two groups present their arguments to see if they are clear about the arguments being put forward and the evidence being provided. Ask for their opinions at the end of the discussion or programme; have they changed their mind about the issue?

REFLECTION & FEEDBACK suggestions

Send some of the children into other classrooms to present one of the arguments prepared by groups. Take a vote from the other classes after they have heard the arguments. Discuss the results afterwards.

GETTING STARTED

Weekend work
Children work in small groups to collaborate on the argument that all 13-year-olds should do a small amount of paid work at the weekends. Ask them to make a list of their arguments as to why this would be a good thing, with a view to presenting their ideas to the class. Remind them they must elaborate on each argument on their list.
After these have been heard, ask if anyone can come up with arguments against this.

Persuasive words
Read through some examples of letters to the editor taken from local newspapers. Invite the class to come up with imagined details about the person who wrote the letters. On a large piece of card, list useful vocabulary found in the letters e.g. I think, some people think, people claim, it is said that, on the other hand, in my opinion, it seems that, it is the case that, firstly, secondly, finally, it is important that, therefore, as a result ... and so on.

Influencing ads
Hold a class discussion on whether advertising aimed at children should be allowed during the breaks in children's television programmes. Divide the class into two; one half arguing for, and the other half against. List their ideas on the board. Take a vote on the issue at the end.

Reporter in the street
Using the statements on Resource Sheet 62, children take on the roles. The reporter in each instance interviews the people in other roles and asks for their response to the statement.

Role-play
Children work in pairs to role-play an argument between a child and a parent as to whether that child should be allowed to have a pet. Invite volunteers to present their role-play to the class. Highlight the features of an argument i.e. introduction of the issue, arguments for and against with supporting evidence and elaboration, reinforcement of the initial point of view.

128   129

For pupils:

Activity Sheets
Up to nine Activity Sheets for each text type unit.

Learning Objective for each activity.

Emphasis on a range of strategies, exploring texts and building appropriate text type structure.

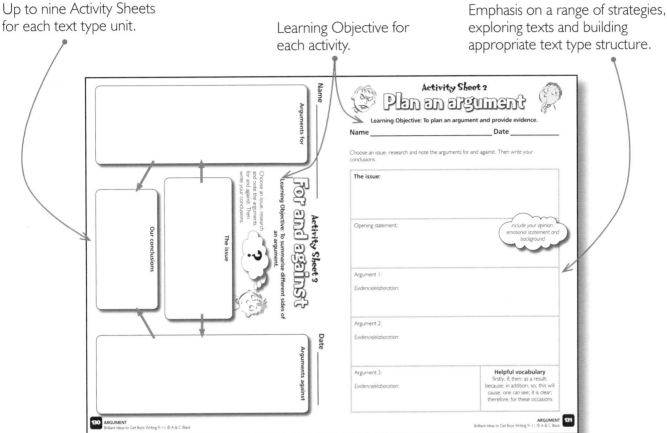

Resource Sheets
Resource Sheets to support and extend engagement with text type.

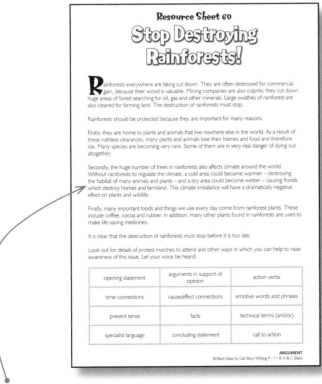

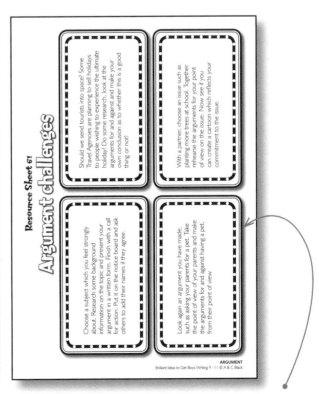

Model text with labels for children to research the text and understand the structure and language features.

Challenge opportunites for children to extend the understanding of the unit.

NARRATIVE FICTION

Narrative fiction is the telling (or narrating) of 'story' using many different forms. It includes the forms of traditional fiction, fold and fairy tales, fables, myths and legends as well as science fiction, fantasy, mystery and adventure, historical and contemporary fiction. Narrative fiction can be presented in many visual forms, including picture books and comic or cartoons.

★ Provide (and read) a range of appropriate texts as models, from genre being studied.
★ Share books which appeal to boys and provide opportunities to respond to them – role-play, dramatisation etc.
★ Provide electronic resources, if appropriate.
★ Create a bank of relevant vocabulary, phrases and prompts which help thinking, planning and reviewing.
★ Use *Talk for writing* principles and lots of opportunity to talk and collaborate prior to and throughout the writing process and dramatic strategies to promote high-quality thinking.
★ Display, demonstrate and discuss model texts and visuals and give a clear purpose for each task. Use genre terminology to ensure clear understanding of text structure and language features.
★ Ensure children discuss and agree text purpose and audience.
★ Provide questions which help the planning process.
★ Make available a range of tools, including ICT tools.
★ Display work in progress and finished work, in many different versions.
★ Ensure opportunites for review and reflection are available and provide effective feedback.

NARRATIVE FICTION
FAMILIAR, HISTORICAL, ADVENTURE AND MYSTERY

Purpose	to interest, entertain and amuse; sometimes also to inform and instruct
Structure	opening or orientation in which characters, setting and time are established; a series of actions and events, with a complication and an ending in which the complication is resolved
Language features	usually past tense, but sometimes present tense; dialogue, descriptive language (use of simile, alliteration, metaphor) and descriptive vocabulary (adjectives, strong verbs); first and third person pronouns
Visual features	may contain illustrations; cartoons (comics)
Examples	*The Hobbit*, by JRR Tolkein; *Fantastic Mr Fox*, by Roald Dahl; *Thunder and Lightnings*, by Jan Mark; *Bill's New Frock*, by Anne Fine; *Spooks Away*, by Sue Purkiss

Cross-curricular suggestions

History
★ Children choose a character from a historical period being studied, describe the character in detail and make a 'Wanted' poster for them.

Art/Geography
★ Children take inspiration for a setting or characters from a piece of art being studied or even a place being studied.

Drama
★ Divide the class into groups and provide them with copies of a piece of narrative from one of the areas of familiar, historical, adventure or mystery. Have the children create a script using lots of dialogue. Make one person in each group the narrator to move the story along when needed. They take turns to present to the class.

Teacher's notes

Use the **Challenge Cards** (Resource Sheet 9) to extend the unit.

The purpose of narratives is to tell (narrate) a sequence of events with problems and conflicts faced by characters in times and places. Narratives can be presented as picture books, cartoons or comics, short stories and longer stories with more complicated plots.

Activity Sheet 1

Talk about stories children like; include different genres and presentations. Display the activity sheet and talk about the structure and features of narratives. Ask the children to give you examples to answer the questions on the sheet. Give the sheet to pairs of children and ask them to answer the questions with reference to a particular book. It may be useful to display or provide pairs with copies of Resource Sheet 1, which they could use to make notes about their chosen book. Are there any other questions which will help them understand the story? Remind children that planning a story, any story, is very important and authors spend time doing this. They should also spend time planning, either by telling the story to a partner, using the Narrative planning frame on Resource Sheet 1 or an 'Events web' (General Reference Sheet), making a story map or drawing the events.

Activity Sheet 2

Read some openings from several books and discuss the effect they have on the reader. Do they 'grab' the reader; does the reader want to hear more? Children look through some books in pairs and compile a list of different openings. These could be added to a class chart with headings such as: action (or in-action); description of people (*Harry Potter and the Philosopher's Stone*); description of place; dialogue (*Charlotte's Web*); an explanation; a sound; questions (*The Iron Man*). Keep the chart for children to refer to later. Discuss whether some openings are better for some types of stories i.e. a sound might be a good opening for a mystery e.g. 'The garage door creaked as he unlocked it, and John froze …' (from *The Circus Runaways* by Margaret Pearce). Give the activity sheet to the children and ask them to work in pairs to write three different openings for an adventure story. Suggest that they talk through the plot first, and possibly role-play some of the opening scenes. Keep these openings, for use on Activity Sheet 8.

Activity Sheet 3

Ask a couple of children to role-play a favourite character for the class. Can they guess who it is? Talk about how authors build characters. They know all about their characters even if they don't use all that knowledge in the text. Display Resource Sheet 2 and ask children to use the headings to discuss a character with a partner. Give children the activity sheet and ask them to create a description of the main character from *Spooks Away*, a novel by Sue Purkiss, in which children go to a remote Scottish castle to make a video and find it haunted. They can use the headings to write a description of Spooker Batt. They then discuss with their partner what might happen in their version of the story, and think about how the character might act and feel. In a plenary session, compare some of the character descriptions and suggest children read the book to see if the author had different ideas for the character.

Activity Sheet 4

Choose a piece of historical fiction and discuss with the children the clues from the text which fix the characters in that historical period. Provide a range of historical fiction titles and ask children in pairs or small groups to pick a character from one of the books. Give them a copy of the activity sheet and ask them to discuss the character descriptions and actions in the text, before completing the sheet. They should search the text for evidence of that character's appearance which give clues as to when the story is set, e.g. clothing, hairstyle, jewellery, etc. Afterwards the children can look for any other ways in which the author indicates the time in which the story was set.

Activity Sheet 5

Discuss the setting for *Spooks Away* and ask children for some strong descriptive words and phrases to describe it. Write these on the board. Display Resource Sheet 3 and discuss where each of the places might be and use the prompts to describe it. Break the class into groups and give each group a genre (familiar, historical, adventure or mystery) and ask them to describe one of the photos as a setting for a story in that genre. Remind them to think about the weather, the time of day and year and the general atmosphere. Give the activity sheet to the children and ask them to work together to make notes and then write a description of the setting. In a plenary session, display some of the descriptions and highlight descriptive words and phrases.

Activity Sheet 6

Choose a well-known story and ask children to relate the events in the story. Make notes on the whiteboard and check the order when they have finished. Display the General Reference sheet 'Events web' and talk about how to describe an event in a story. Working in small groups, children choose a setting (using ideas on Resource Sheet 4 if necessary) and some characters. Give the activity sheet to the groups and ask them to discuss and then make notes for the plot of a story. (General Reference Sheet 'Chain of events' can be used by some children to draw the events.) Give each group 15 minutes to discuss their event and then make their notes. Then ask each member of the group to 'flesh out' one of the events and draft it on the computer. When the group reconvenes, read all of the drafts, discuss and agree changes. Think about good words and phrases to link the events together into one piece.

Activity Sheet 7

Talk about direct speech in stories, display some examples or look at books children are reading. What do they notice? Give pairs of children a piece of written speech, or use the text at the bottom of Resource Sheet 5. Children decide who the speakers are and what the situation might be, role-play the conversation and continue it. Display the text and discuss who was speaking, when they started and stopped and how we know that. Were other things happening while they were speaking? How do they know? Highlight the use of quotation marks, commas at the end of speech, new lines for new speakers. Then display the four scenarios and ask pairs to choose one. They can add a second frame and then act out the scenario, recording the conversation. Give them the activity sheet and ask them to complete it together, then write the conversation in their books, using the punctuation you have discussed.

Activity Sheet 8

Take a well-known tale such as *Jack and the Beanstalk* or *Red Riding Hood* and ask children in groups of three to each take a character from the tale and tell it from that character's point of view. After children have role-played or told the tale to each other, they discuss the differences between the three points of view. Remind children about the bank robbery they wrote about in Activity 2. Display the activity sheet and discuss the task. Children should 'replay' the bank robbers (talk and role-play) to make notes about the experience for two others characters from the events. They then write an ending from one of those characters' points of view – remind them to use third person pronouns.

Activity Sheets 9 and 10

These two sheets can be used together, the first as a planning sheet and the second to begin the writing process and to think about improving the writing. Give children the activity sheet but before beginning, take time to discuss and role-play the scenario (or choose an alternative from Resource Sheet 6). It is important that they record the discussions as these could be helpful when making notes on the sheet and when they begin writing. The prompts will help children to begin, but they should not constrict their discussions. When they move on to Activity 10 and begin to write parts of their story on the activity sheet, encourage them to look at Resource Sheet 7 for good connectives, and to always look for better words. The General Reference Sheets 'Making it better' and 'Proofreading' could be displayed to help them improve and re-draft their work before moving to a polished version.

REFLECTION & FEEDBACK suggestions

Suggest that children talk about their narratives with others and accept suggestions constructively. Using computer programs to lay out and illustrate writing can help children to value their work, as can reading their narratives to the class or to other classes in the school.

11

GETTING STARTED

Make lists

When talking about the books children enjoy, look for features and make lists which can be used later, such as 'Top 10 character descriptions', 'Quotable quotes' (Resource Sheet 8) or best 'surprises' / 'twists in the story'. These can be displayed when children are writing, or stored on the computer where children can access them.

What is it?

Provide a range of novels, or extracts, with titles and covers obscured. Ask children to read and think about each novel and discuss with a partner or group whether they think it is an adventure, a mystery, a fantasy or a historical novel. Why do they think that? Encourage them to explain their decisions using words and phrases from the novel.

Discuss characterisation

Choose a character from a well-known story e.g. *Harry Potter*. Together with the class brainstorm all the information the reader knows about this character. Use the whiteboard to create a character map. How has the author managed to convey all this information – through rich description, dialogue, plot …? Provide quotes from the text to back up findings.

Missing scene!

Ask the children in pairs to pick an adventure or mystery story that they know. They must draw a six-frame story board of this narrative, missing out one of the six frames. They then swap with another group, who must fill in the blank scene.

Snapshot drama

Pick a moment from a text you have read. Capture it as a freeze frame. Divide the children into groups to act out that piece as a mini drama. Ask them to think about what is going on for each of the characters in the frame. Ask them to consider what has just happened and what is about to happen.

Tell a story

Agree an outline plot for a class story and ask one child to begin. Other children pick up the story, using a connective, such as 'although', 'then', 'fortunately', 'despite' etc. The connectives could be picked from a set of cards, or from a list, see Resource Sheet 7.

Talking about narratives

Learning Objective: To interrogate a text to deepen and clarify understanding and response.

Name _____ **Date** _____

Choose a favourite narrative and talk to a partner about what makes it a great story. Use the questions to think about the story and the writer's craft.

Title:

★ Why do you think it is a good story?

★ How does the author capture the attention of the reader?

★ Does the story have a strong beginning?

★ Did the author create interesting characters?

★ Were the characters believable?

★ How has the author introduced the main character?

★ What words and phrases did the author use to describe the character?

★ Did the author create a vivid description of the setting for the story?

★ Has the author used dialogue to tell you about the character or the setting?

★ Were there any surprises in the text?

★ Did the ending 'wrap up' the story?

★ Why do you think the author wrote the narrative?

And when you are the author…

What is the easiest part of writing your own story?

What is the hardest part of writing your own story?

Why do you write stories?

Beginnings

Learning Objective: To recognise the differences between narrative types.

Name _____ **Date** _____

A story opening is the best place to grab your readers' attention. How will you start? With action, description or dialogue? Use strong descriptive words, but don't tell the reader everything - you want them to read on!

Title:
Plot: _You are walking down the street (are you really there or is it a dream?). Three men are running from the bank and they jump into a car. What have they done? Do you know them? Or have you found a clue?_

Opening with action	**Opening with a description of people or place**	**Opening with dialogue**

'Spooky' character

Learning Objective: To make notes about a character from a story, before writing a polished version.

Name _____ **Date** _____

Talk to your partner about how you see 'Spooker Batt'. Then use the headings to make notes to give you all the information you need to write a description of him. Write a description of 'Spooker Batt' using your notes. Read it to your partner, make changes, then write a polished version and display it with a drawing of the character.

> It was 'so-o-o' hard getting up for the first day of term after the long summer holidays. Spooker Batt, ghost-in-training, turned over and buried his head under his pillow, hoping the noise and the nagging would go away…

Name:	
Personal details:	
Appearance:	
Personality:	
Qualities and talents:	
Likes and dislikes:	

A character from the past

Learning Objective: To use details and quotes from the text to fix a character in a historical setting.

Name _____ **Date** _____

Title of story:

Setting (when and where):

Character's appearance: *Details which fix the time and place of the story.*	Evidence from the text: *List details and quotes.*

General clues from the character, provided in the text through actions or speech and vocabulary:

Where is it set?

Learning Objective: To generate vocabulary and imagery to describe a setting and to write a description.

Name _____ **Date** _____

Make notes of good words and phrases to describe your setting on the concept map. Use words which will help convey to your reader the type of narrative you are writing. Write sentences using similes, metaphors and personification.

Narrative type:

Setting:

Image sentences:

With your group, use your notes to write a description of the setting. Read it aloud and make changes before writing a polished version.

What happens?

Learning Objective: To create a story plot by making decisions about the events of the story.

Name _____ Date _____

Choose a setting and some characters. Make notes about the events in your story.

Title:	
Who are the main characters?	Where is it set?
What happens? Write a summary sentence.	

List the events in order.	1st event
Is there a conflict or problem?	2nd event
How is it resolved?	3rd event
Is there a surprise or twist?	4th event
When does it happen?	5th event
Don't forget suspense, between events.	6th event

Activity Sheet 7
They said!

Learning Objective: To focus on how the author creates a clear and effective setting.

Name _____ Date _____

Choose one of the scenarios on Resource Sheet 5 and give the two characters names. Act out the scene between them. Make notes of your conversation.

What's happening in the scene?	
Character's name:	**Character's name:**
•	•
•	•
•	•
•	•
•	•

Other words for 'said':

Good adverbs to use:

When you are agreed on the conversation, write it out on a separate sheet. Remember to use quotation marks around the speech and a comma after the speech. Start a new line when you change speakers.

Activity Sheet 8
Point of view

Learning Objective: To understand that narratives can be written from different points of view.

Name _____ Date _____

How might the bank robbery have ended?

> *But on Sunday, I didn't feel like playing in the garden. I couldn't forget all the action and the noise of the events last Thursday. It was just an ordinary day which was turned topsy-turvy, but it was exciting! After all, I had seen the bank robbers leaving the scene and I remembered the get-away car. I even had a mention on the TV news – a member of the public helping police with their enquiries.*
>
> *So I deserved an afternoon, just remembering!*

Think about two of the other people involved in the action – one of the bank robbers, a bank worker or a customer in the bank. Make some notes about how they felt, what they saw and did. Choose one of them and write an ending from their point of view, but remember you are writing it, not them.

bank robber	someone in the bank

What were you doing?

How were you involved?

How did you feel at the time / afterwards?

How did it end for you?

What happened afterwards?

Remember
When you write the ending for one of these characters you will be writing in the 3rd person. Make a list of 3rd person pronouns to use.

Brilliant Ideas to Get Boys Writing 9–11 © A & C Black

Making the notes

Learning Objective: To make notes for an adventure or mystery narrative.

Name _____ **Date** _____

Make notes in the boxes to help you write a story about being shipwrecked. Write down as much detail as you can, and think about useful words.

Title:

Characters:

How many characters?

Who is the main character?

Qualities important in this situation

Appearance and personality

How do they interact?

Setting:

Which boat were you on?

Where are you now?

What do you see, hear, smell and feel?

Plot:

What happened before?

What is going to happen?

Problem:

Resolution:

How can it be resolved?

Is there going to be a problem?

Who is going to resolve it?

Good words:

Drafting and checking

Learning Objective: To begin writing sections of a narrative and consider changes and improvements.

Name _____ **Date** _____

Draft your text in the boxes. Then think about how you can improve it.

Beginning: Remember to grab the readers' attention.

Middle: Describe all the events. Think about the order.

Ending: 'Wrap up' the story for the reader.

Nuts and bolts

★ Look at the words you have used. Can you use better words – stronger, richer?

★ Look at the sentences. Can you add words to make them more descriptive and exciting?

★ Check the spelling and word usage.

★ Do you have enough detail, but not too much?

★ Can you split the text into more paragraphs?

★ Have you included dialogue?

★ Read it to a friend. Can you improve it?

★ Re-draft it and write a polished version.

TRADITIONAL TALES

Purpose	to interest, entertain and amuse; to convey a message or moral; to explain natural phenomena; originated in oral form
Structure	opening or orientation in which characters, setting and time are established; a series of actions and events, with at least one complication, resolution and ending; may include a theme or message, e.g. good versus evil, courage, hard work or honesty
Language features	past tense; dialogue; limited description of characters or settings; strong verbs; sometimes repetition; third person pronouns
Visual features	may include illustrations; cartoon and comic versions
Examples	Folk and fairy tales, fables, myths and legends from a wide range of cultures. Modern versions such as *Anancy and Mr Dry-Bone*, by Fiona French; *Little Red Riding Hood*, by Tony Ross; *The Story Thief*, by Andrew Fusek Peters; *The Barber's Clever Wife,* by Narinder Dhami

Cross-curricular suggestions

Geography
★ Children research the traditional tales of countries being studied. They compare them with other well-known traditional tales.

Drama
★ In groups, children work on a re-telling of a traditional tale, dramatise the tale into a short play which they rehearse and perform to the class.

Art
★ Children produce artwork to reflect the stories and messages found in selected tales. Look at Greek vases and the legends told on them, pictorially. They could create a design for a Greek vase depicting a legend.

Teacher's notes

Use the **Challenge Cards** (Resource Sheet 18) to extend the unit.

Activity Sheet 1

Make available a range of traditional tales, including all forms from a range of cultures and modern editions and parodies. Discuss the origin of traditional tales, from an oral tradition with motifs which are often common across cultures. Ask children, in groups, to choose a tale and 'tell' it to another class – by recording it. Recap, in discussion, the structure and the features of traditional tales. Display Resource Sheet 10 and highlight the features with examples from texts. If necessary, review the model texts (Resource Sheets 11-14). Give pairs the activity sheet and ask them to choose a folk or fairy tale, to identify the structure and features, then complete the sheet with reference to the text. They then compare with another pair or with another tale. The sheet could be used, with slight changes to questions, to investigate fables, myths or legends.

Activity Sheet 2

Recap, in class discussion, the structure of a traditional tale. Divide the class into pairs or small groups, giving each a copy of a different traditional tale. Ask the children to discuss their tale and re-tell it to each other. Using the activity sheet, they identify the structure and the theme and make notes on the sheet. They then swap a part of their tale (the orientation, the complication or the resolution) with another group and see what difference it makes to their tale. If time permits, give each group another version of the same tale and ask them to compare the two. After discussion about tales, display Resource Sheet 15 and ask children to write a new version of the tale using one or more of these innovations.

Activity Sheet 3

Read a selection of parodies of traditional tales (e.g. Tony Ross's *Little Red Riding Hood*) and modern tales to the class. Ask the children to discuss, in small groups, what aspects are based on the original tales and to identify the differences. Introduce the term 'parody' and discuss what it means. Give the activity sheet to children and ask them, in pairs, to write down the structure of a tale (folk and fairy tales have the greatest variety of source texts). They can discuss the changes they want to make and make notes on the sheet: changes to actions, character personalities, plot or ending for a parody; or changing characters and settings into recognisable modern versions with attributes for a modern version. Some children will find a modern version easier than a parody. Give children time to draft, review and then finish their tales.

Activity Sheet 4

Display original fables (Aesop and La Fontaine) and modern versions (Leo Lionni) for the children to read, discuss and act out. Ask them what the 'morals' are in the fables, in their own words, and make a class list. Then make a list of morals they could use to write their own fables, in small groups e.g. 'it pays to tell the truth'; 'co-operation gets results'; 'trees watch over us', etc. Remind children that animals and the elements are often given human characteristics in fables. Arrange the children in small groups with the activity sheet for their notes. They can use the notes to write their fable as a short radio script or as a six-frame cartoon. They then draft their work and, when finished, record or illustrate it – make sure each member of the group is participating. Make a display with other published fables.

Activity Sheet 5

Read a variety of myths and legends and discuss the origin and purpose of each. Compare the differences say between Greek and Scandinavian myths, myths from the British Isles and those from indigenous tribes. Ask children to choose a myth or legend, discuss it with a partner, then re-tell or role-play it to another pair. Make a list of characters (heroes) from legends (e.g.

Finn McCool, Odysseus, Daedalus & Icarus, Odin, King Arthur). Talk about the qualities often associated with heroes – strength, bravery, fearlessness, valiant deeds, amazing powers – and list these for children to use later. Ask each child to choose one hero and create a profile of the hero to create a 'Wanted' poster. Ask them to think about what they know about the hero, find out as much as they can and make notes of words or phrases from the text which will be useful. Give them the activity sheet for their notes and display Resource Sheet 16 to help them decide what information they will need. Give them time to gather the information and make and illustrate the poster (using the computer, if appropriate). In a plenary session, discuss the posters and decide which would best achieve the purpose and why.

Activity Sheet 6

Look at a number of versions of Beowulf in narrative form, including graphic and illustrated versions such as *Beowulf*, by Michael Morpurgo; *Beowulf: Master Slayer*, by Storrie & Randall; *Beowulf: Dragonslayer*, by Sutcliff & Keeping; *Beowulf and Grendel*, by Waddell & Howells and *Beowulf the Brave*, by Julia Green. Give children time to read at least one version and make a list of the events. Discuss the importance of raising the reader's interest by increasing and decreasing the 'excitement' value of events. They then put their list of events in order on a graph from 1-10 showing excitement. Display Resource Sheet 17 to help them and discuss differences of opinion. Ask children to choose another myth or legend and make a list of events with a partner and add them to the graph on the activity sheet. Children then share and discuss their graphs.

Activity Sheet 7

With the class, decide on a group of characters (heroes and villains), and a setting. (If necessary agree a conflict and resolution or provide a range of different ones – someone acquires a gift with magical powers; a quest to find a magical object; the rescue of an important person; someone gets lost then found again – or this can be left to the groups.) Divide children into groups of four and ask them to discuss the elements for their story. Give out the activity sheet for them to make notes. Suggest that they first write profiles of the main heroes and villains, and possibly draw an image, then create the setting, before moving on to the events and the conflict and resolution. Ask them to create a story map of the events, and to think about the increasing and decreasing excitement of their story. Make sure children discuss their notes and possibly role-play some of the events and make lists of usable words before they start writing. The drafting of the myth/legend could be divided among group members, which would allow for text to be swapped and revised collaboratively. Give a time limit for each task. When the work is polished, use a suitable software package to write the final version. Make a display, including the character profiles, the setting descriptions, illustrations, drafts and the finished work.

REFLECTION & FEEDBACK suggestions

Suggest that children discuss their drafts with others and accept suggestions constructively before finishing their pieces. They can use computer programs to lay out and illustrate their work. This can help them to value their finished work, as can reading their narratives to the class or to other classes in the school.

Change the character.

The children re-tell orally a well known story, but substitute different characteristics in a certain character e.g. *The Three Billy Goats* where the troll is kind and helpful; *Robin Hood* where Robin is nasty …

What is it?

Children draw a scene or a character which could come from a traditional tale, it doesn't have to be a well known one. These are put into a hat. Everyone draws one out and then tells a short tale including that scene or character.

Tell it again

Put a few traditional tale titles in a hat e.g. *Robin Hood*, *The Three Little Pigs*, *The Three Billy Goats Gruff*, *Cinderella* … Ask for volunteers to pick a title and re-tell the story from a certain character's point of view.

Myth messages

Collect and read myths from ancient Greece and ancient Scandinavia in a group. Compare and contrast the characters and the message being conveyed by the fables; present these to the class.

Record it

In pairs, children choose two characters from a traditional tale. They record a conversation between the characters and then ask the class to listen to the recording and say who they think the characters are.

Tell a story together.

Someone chooses a well known tale and provides the first sentence, starting with 'Once Upon A Time ....'. Carry on round the class with each child contributing a sentence until the story is complete.

Tale ingredients

In pairs or small groups, make lists (on the computer) of ingredients for traditional tales e.g. particular character types (warrior, handsome prince, good fairy), magical objects found in tales (wand, cloak, ball, mirror), themes and values constantly used in tales (good triumphing over evil/hard work winning through, courage, honesty being rewarded, trickery).

Activity Sheet 1
Traditional tale

Learning Objective: To recognise the structure and features of different forms of traditional tales.

Name _____ **Date** _____

With a partner choose a traditional tale and answer the questions about it. When you have finished you can compare this tale with another traditional tale.

Title:

Where is it from?

What is it about (plot)?

What does the introduction (orientation) tell you?

What is the conflict?

How is it resolved?

Is there any repetition?

What is the theme?

What patterns or motifs are in the tale?

Are there lots of versions of the tale?

What are the similarities and differences?

Is the tale found in other media?

TRADITIONAL TALES
Brilliant Ideas to Get Boys Writing 9–11 © A & C Black

Activity Sheet 2

Focus on structure and theme

Learning Objective: To identify the elements of a traditional tale.

Name _____ **Date** _____

Read through a traditional tale together with your group and discuss the text. Identify the main structural features below. Is there a message or theme in this narrative?

Orientation:

Characters:

Setting:

Series of events:

Complication:

Resolution:

Theme or message:

A new version

Learning objective: To construct a parody or a modern version of a traditional tale.

Name _____ **Date** _____

Choose a traditional tale, discuss it with your partner and make notes of its structure. Then agree what you want to keep and what would be fun to change for your new version (a parody or a modern version) and make notes of the changes.

	Original tale	**New version**
Title: *Has it changed?*		
Orientation: *Do you signal your changes?* *Is the setting changed?*		
Characters: *Are there the same characters?* *Are they altered?*		
Events: *How are they altered?* *Are there new events?* *Are they in different places?*		
Complication: *Same or altered?*		
Resolution: *Is it a shock?*		

On a separate piece of paper, draw up a profile for each of your characters and draw a story map to show the action. Now with the changes in mind write a draft of your new version of the tale, check it before writing a polished version to share with others.

Activity Sheet 4
A fable

Learning Objective: To understand the structure and features of fables and to construct one.

Name _____ Date _____

Make notes about your fable in the table.

Moral:		
Characters:		
Setting:		
Plot:		
Title:		

Animal, elements or human characters?

What are their characteristics?

Describe the setting:

Use for sound effects or illustrations.

What happens?

Create 'frames' to tell the fable.

Use your notes to draft your fable as a short radio play or a cartoon. When you have read and corrected your draft, write a finished version and either record the play or illustrate your cartoon.

Legend fact file

Learning Objective: To understand and develop a character.

Name _____ **Date** _____

Make notes about the character you have chosen. Make sure you get lots of detail as you will need to use your notes to create the 'Wanted' poster.

Character's name:
Where is the character?
Background information:
Family:
Friends:
Lives:
What does your character look like?
What kind of person is your character?
How does your character feel? How do they react?
Good words to describe your character.

WANTED

?

Name _____

Date _____

Activity Sheet 6

Changing pace

Learning Objective: To identify the changing pace in a myth or legend and be able to plot it on a graph.

Choose a myth or legend and make a note of the events. Give each of the events a rating to show how exciting each one is. Does the hero display heroic qualities? Do the events build the mystery and suspense?

1

2

3

4

5

6

7

8

9

10

| 1 | = not exciting | 10 | = very exciting |

Myths and legends

Learning Objective: To work as a group to create a myth or legend.

Name _____ Date _____

Discuss your myth/legend with your group and make notes of your discussions. Remember to include good descriptive words and powerful verbs. Create a profile of each of the main characters.

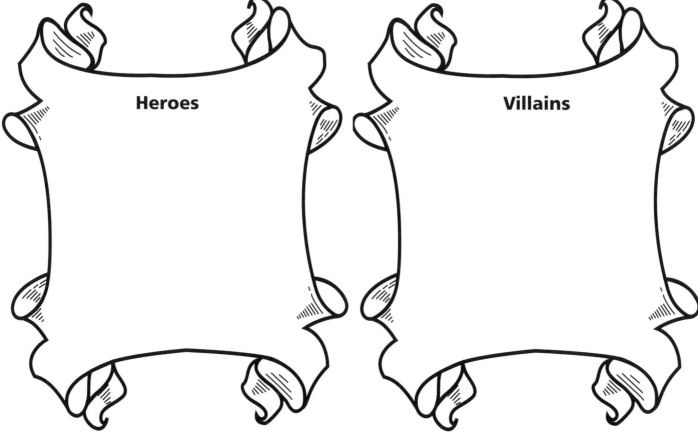

Heroes

Villains

Setting Does the setting influence the action? Create a word or pictorial description.	
Events and Complication What is in your orientation? Draw a story map of the main events.	
Find a Resolution Is this the end of the tale?	
Message	

TRADITIONAL TALES
Brilliant Ideas to Get Boys Writing 9–11 © A & C Black

OTHER CULTURES

Purpose	to interest, entertain and amuse; sometimes also to inform
Structure	opening or orientation in which characters, setting and time are established; a series of actions and events, with a complication and an ending in which the complication is resolved
Language features	descriptive language to create vivid images, first/third person, past tense, dialogue usually past tense, but sometimes present tense; direct and reported speech; descriptive language (literal and figurative language); first and third person pronouns
Visual features	may include illustrations
Examples	*My Childhood*, by Maxim Gorky; *Granny Ting Ting*, by Patrice Lawrence; *Ever Clever Eva*, by Andrew Fusek Peters; *Bamba Beach*, by Patima Mitchell, *Village by the Sea*, by Anita Desai; *Little Soldier*, by Bernard Ashley; *The Wheel of Surya*, by Jamila Gavin; *Out of the World* series, by Catherine Baker

Cross-curricular suggestions

Drama
★ Narrate a story from another culture which the children can then work on in small groups to present as a drama.

Art
★ Children use the text of a narrative from a different culture to inspire a piece of artwork, perhaps to provide a backdrop to a display of written work.

Music
★ Try to find some pieces of music from the relevant culture when discussing a text, to immerse the children completely in this different world.

Teacher's notes

Use the **Challenge Cards** (Resource Sheet 23) to extend the unit.

Activity Sheet 1

Recap on traditional tales – they often come from different cultures yet sometimes have the same motifs, conflict/ resolutions. Narratives from other cultures follow the same structure as other narratives: orientation, introduction of characters and setting; series of events; complication and ultimate resolution. Choose a short story from another culture to read to the class or use Resource Sheet 19. Discuss the structure and how you know it's from another culture – names (including author's name), actions (having to go outside to the toilet, carrying a rifle), relationships (Uncle Mikhail living with family), setting (snow shoes) etc. In pairs, children draw a story map of the events ('Chain of events' Reference Sheet could be used), then use the activity sheet to make notes on the cultural vocabulary and action, including those which are implied.

Activity Sheet 2

Ask the children to put themselves in the shoes of the author (Maxim Gorky or author used in the previous activity). They start with an event in the story (Uncle Mikhail returning to the house with his hair on end and his eyes popping out) and consider alternative events to continue the story. Encourage them to discuss and role-play lots of options, and to continue on the back of the sheet if they need to. Remind them to use the customs and attitudes etc. from the culture, making a list of words and phrases. How will their story finish? When they have outlined the events in their story, they draft and then write their revised version.

Activity Sheet 3

Using the descriptions of characters and setting and their knowledge of the culture they have discussed in the previous two activities, children write a letter as the character in the story (Maxim Gorky in rural Russia, or other characters they have been working with). They are writing to their cousin who lives in another country. Children make notes about what they will tell their cousin, and make sure they include how they feel about the events they describe. Discuss the letters, and help children to

REFLECTION & FEEDBACK suggestions

Ask children to reflect on what they found difficult in writing a story about another culture, and ask them how important it was to research the background of the culture. Ask children to read a story from another culture from the library and to review it for the class, giving a synopsis and details about how the author provided the important information about the culture for the reader.

understand the importance of 'being' in the other culture, and note examples of cultural detail that may have been included.

Activity Sheet 4

Look at the pictures of the boys from other cultures on Resource Sheet 20 and the two story orientations. Talk about these children and how are they the same or different from themselves. Give children the opportunity to role-play situations they think the boys might encounter. Ask children to choose one set of characters, and with a writing partner, make notes about these characters on the activity sheet. These characters will be used to write a story from another culture, so the details are important. Suggest the children also think about what kinds of things the boys may be saying to each other; groups role-play some conversations and make notes on the back of the sheet.

Activity Sheet 5

Following on from Activity 4, ask children to describe the setting from another culture for their story – this can be from a photo or a description such as those on Resource Sheets 21 or 22. Suggest they begin by considering how their setting is the same and different from the settings they know, and give them the opportunity to research the setting, using the library or the internet. Give the activity sheet to pairs of children and suggest they make as many notes as possible, even if they may not use direct reference to the setting in their story.

Activity Sheet 6

Using the detail of the characters and setting developed in Activities 4 and 5, children now plan their story in their writing pairs. As a group, talk about the structure of the narrative and discuss the importance of the conflict and resolution in their story – the conflict might be something which is only possible in that culture (a hurricane, being lost at a religious festival etc.). Give pairs the activity sheet and suggest that they role-play some possible events and conflict/resolution scenarios which will help them make notes. Remind them that they should NOT begin writing until they have completed their notes. Supply the General Reference Sheets 'Making it better' and 'Proofreading' to children when they are working on their drafts.

Activity Sheet 7

Begin by looking at illustrations from different cultures, including Manga comics. Discuss how some cultures can use a particular format in storytelling, such as Manga comic illustrations from Japan. Explain that Japan has been producing stories with pictures for hundreds of years, but Manga came about in the 1940s, after World War 2, when US soldiers were stationed in Japan and the Japanese discovered the comic! Now two billion Manga comic books are sold each year in Japan. Discuss the use of the visual to tell the story. Give pairs of children the activity sheet and ask them to decide on a 'frame' or event from their story to re-tell using a cartoon picture and dialogue, with their text beside it. Then ask children to choose a six or eight frame layout and work on turning a story into a Manga style cartoon. Display the layout plans and finished work together.

GETTING STARTED

Listen to this

Collect a range of stories from different cultures for children to refer to. Divide them into groups and give a different story to each group. Ask them to discuss their text, make some notes and present a short synopsis to the rest of the class, highlighting culturally specific vocabulary, customs and attitudes.

Tell me a story

Invite adults with experience of other cultures to read or tell a story to the class from that culture. They will be able to provide cultural background and context for culturally specific vocabulary and events. Ask children to bring in text from other cultures which are part of their own family background, to share with the class. Use a map to highlight where the stories take place.

Setting

Choose a setting from another culture from a book. Ask children to describe the setting. They then make a list of descriptive adjectives and write a description which could be used as a background for a play or film taking place in that setting.

How do you live?

Choose a culture e.g. West African, Asian, Scandinavian. Ask the children to choose a character that lives in the culture, research the culture and create a profile of the character and their life. They should make notes about all the different aspects of the character's life, using the library and the internet to help in their research.

Hot seat

In pairs, children choose a character from a story set in another culture. One child assumes the role of the character and the other asks questions about the culture and how it is different from their own. Encourage children to use quotes from the book.

Story from another culture

Learning Objective: To deduce differences in characters, cultures and traditions.

Name _____ **Date** _____

Read a story from another culture and draw a story map to show the events. Look for words, phrases and actions which tell you the story is from another culture and write them in the boxes.

Title:

Characters:

Setting:

Orientation:

Events:

Complication and resolution:

Story from another culture

Learning Objective: To use authentic cultural details to create an alternative ending to a story.

Name _____ Date _____

Consider how you could continue the story. Discuss some options with a writing partner. Use characters, relationships and actions from the culture to help you.

Write your story in your book. Make sure you have a strong ending.

> One night Uncle Mikhail went out to the lavatory and suddenly came running back, his hair on end, his eyes popping out, and too paralysed to say anything.

Words to describe the culture:

Activity Sheet 3
Dear Cousin

Learning Objective: To use authentic details of another culture to write a letter in role.

Name _____ **Date** _____

Before you begin your letter, make notes about the events you want to describe to your cousin. Remember to include information and details about your culture that will explain how you feel about the people and the events.

Address

Date

Greeting

Sign off

Draft your letter here. Read it to a friend, make changes, then write your finished letter on another sheet or on the computer.

Characters from another culture

Learning Objective: To describe characters from another culture.

Name _____ **Date** _____

Use the boxes to describe the characters for your story from another culture. Include details which place the characters in that culture.

Name:
Description
(appearance, personality and attitudes)

Relationships
(family)
(to other characters)

Likes and dislikes

Thinks and feels

Name:
Description
(appearance, personality and attitudes)

Relationships
(family)
(to other characters)

Likes and dislikes

Thinks and feels

Name:
Description
(appearance, personality and attitudes)

Relationships
(family)
(to other characters)

Likes and dislikes

Thinks and feels

Name:
Description
(appearance, personality and attitudes)

Relationships
(family)
(to other characters)

Likes and dislikes

Thinks and feels

Who is going to be your main character? _____

The story will be from whose point of view? _____

Activity Sheet 5
Setting from another culture

Learning Objective: To describe settings from another culture.

Name _____ **Date** _____

Decide on the setting for your story and make your notes. Research the setting first to be sure you have all the information you need.

Setting:

What words would you use to describe …			
The sights?	The sounds?	The smells?	The atmosphere?

What words and phrases would you use to describe …		
The weather?	The landscape?	The living conditions?

Write a short description of the setting. Remember you don't have to describe it all!	Words and phrases which bring it alive:

Drafting a story

Learning Objective: To research and plan a story from another culture.

Name _____ **Date** _____

Use the characters and setting you have developed to write a story set in another culture. Plan your story and make notes of the events in the boxes.

Title: _____

Characters

Setting

Orientation
Introduce your characters and setting. Make sure it is relevant to the culture.

Event

Event

Complication

Resolution and ending

Write a comic script

Learning Objective: To use a different story-telling format.

Name _____ Date _____

Look at the difference between the cartoon and the text. Do they say the same thing?

Draw your scene or event as a cartoon, with speech bubbles. Write the text beside the illustration.

FILM NARRATIVE

Purpose	to entertain, amuse, interest; sometimes to narrate a story, sometimes to inform or instruct
Structure	opening in which characters and setting are established; a series of actions and events, with a complication and an ending in which the complication is resolved
Language features	dialogue and sometimes narration
Visual features	visual depiction of characters, setting and time; film meta language use to create mood, viewpoint, suspense etc. in the narrative; sometimes animation
Examples	Shrek; Finding Nemo; Babe; Ice Age; Where the Wild Things Are; Fantastic Mr Fox; Wind in the Willows

Cross-curricular suggestions

Art
★ Children produce a poster advertising a film which they have seen recently.

Music
★ Children choose a film which they have enjoyed. They find some suitable music to accompany the opening titles of the film on the internet and download it, or compose a short piece of their own to accompany the opening titles. They present the titles and music to the class and ask for their opinions.

History
★ Choose a film known to the class, set sometime in the past. To put the events of the film into context, children research real life events happening at the time this film was set.

Teacher's notes

Use the **Challenge Cards** (Resource Sheet 27) to extend the unit.

Activity Sheet 1

Begin by discussing the books children know that have been made into films, try to keep it as current as possible. Many have been made into animated films: *Where the Wild Things Are* and *Fantastic Mr Fox*; but there are also dramas: the *Harry Potter* films, *Goodnight Mr Tom*, *The Lion the Witch and the Wardrobe*. Illicit from children the fact that films are usually narratives, like fiction, and they have a similar structure with features such as characters, series of events, complication and resolution but they communicate them using visual images, sound and light rather than words. Choose the film of a book which the class has watched, e.g. *The Sheep Pig* by Dick King-Smith, which became *Babe*, or another. Discuss the film and, if time permits, allow children time to role-play some of the situations from the film, and see how they compare to the book descriptions. Give the resource sheet to pairs or small groups and ask them to compare the book with the film version, using the prompts on the sheet. Encourage them to discuss each point, referring back to both the book and the film. Focus on the differences between the text descriptions of people, settings, events etc. and the visual, sound and lighting devices used in the film. In a plenary session ask children to explain their preference for either the film or the book. Use Resource Sheet 24 to review a film if time permits.

Activity Sheet 2

Put the children in small groups and give them access to a range of films to watch. If possible ensure that each group has watched a different film (include both animation and drama). Display the activity sheet and discuss the 'features of film making'. Give a copy of the activity sheet to each group and ask them to make notes about the film they have watched to complete the sheet. They then join with another group and describe to each other the film craft they observed, using examples from the film.

Activity Sheet 3

In pairs or small groups, children choose a character from a film or book. (The titles on Resource Sheet 25 can be used as prompts.) They talk about their character and role-play some of the character's actions. Using the activity sheet, they then write notes for a description of their character; building up all the aspects to create the character. Encourage them to talk about: costume and make-up; mannerisms (walk, talk etc.); speech (accent, particular laugh etc.); actions and attitude; what 'characteristics' they can discern and how? Suggest they have an image of the character, with physical characteristics noted. If they have chosen a character from a book, they may find useful words and phrases in the book. In groups of four, children choose one of their characters to interview for a fan magazine. Ask them to make notes of the questions they want to ask, such as questions about other characters in the story, the situations for the character and how they feel. They should try to avoid questions that can be answered with just 'Yes' or 'No'. When they have written their questions they then 'interview' the character and record the interview.

Activity Sheet 4

Show a couple of minutes of a film (animation or drama) without sound. Ask the children to discuss and role-play (in pairs or groups) what they think is being said. Then listen to the dialogue and discuss the differences between the children's role-play and the film. Then show another clip and, using the activity sheet, children write the dialogue for this clip as speech, using the conventions of dialogue. When they have finished, ask a couple of pairs to role-play their dialogue for the class before watching the original film dialogue.

Activity Sheet 5

Working in pairs, children produce the storyboard for a cartoon animation, suitable for Reception children. (The titles on Resource Sheet 25 can be used as prompts.) They can use simple graphics and speech bubbles to depict the action, although encourage them to write paragraphs to accompany each frame. They decide on a hero who would appeal to young children and a simple storyline. The hero could be modelled on an existing cartoon character or one they invent – Danny the smiling dragon; Flavio the car that roars! The plot can be based on those found on children's television e.g. lost/ found; a surprise gift; a new pet. Children could make a list of alternatives and survey Reception children, before making their decision. They should start by making notes on the activity sheet and using the prompts for their discussions, before moving onto their storyboards. The storyboards should be refined and polished before being read to Reception classes for their feedback. It may be possible to use software to create a short animation from the storyboard, adding speech in balloons or as voice-over. The animation and the story boards can then be displayed.

REFLECTION & FEEDBACK suggestions

Invite children to record a film review for a radio or television programme. Ask them to work with a partner to make notes for their review, and to draft it before delivering it as an oral review. Use the criteria developed in the Getting Started activity.

Getting Started

And the winner is ...

As a class, write some criteria for judging films – the actual categories from BAFTA or the Oscars could even be used here. Then choose three or four recent films which the children are likely to have seen and vote for the categories. In a class discussion, justify the reasons for voting. Perhaps this can be extended to a whole school vote with the class preparing a voting sheet to be distributed to other classes. The sheet could include each of the different categories and the films suggested for each award.

Story board

Choose a scene from a film (or a 15 minute segment) and ask children to prepare a story board for it. What extra notes would they have to add? Suggest character descriptions, characteristics and costumes, set descriptions, dialogue, actions etc.

Who am I?

Using clothing and props from a varied dressing up box, the children can take it in turns to dress up as a character and act out a part with no speaking. Can the rest of the class guess who the person is?

Hot seat

Ask children to pick a familiar character from an agreed list. Ask the rest of the class to think of questions to ask the character. Record the questions and the answers if possible, so that children can use the information gained for characterisation work later.

Role-play

Put the names of some well-known film characters into a container (photos or pictures of characters could be substituted for names). Ask pairs of children to each pick a character; give them two minutes to prepare a conversation between them, with actions, to present to the class. Alternatively, the conversation could be recorded and played back for the class, who could be asked to guess the names of the characters.

Freeze frame

Ask children to look at films with a partner and choose a point to stop the film. They then ask other children 'what happens next?' in the film. They record the responses as notes or with a video camera. Play the next scene in the film and check against the responses. Alternatively, choose a scene from a film or a short segment of action and stop at an exciting or dramatic point. Ask the children, in small groups, to discuss what they think happens next and act out the subsequent action. Watch the efforts of each group and then watch the next part of the actual film. Who was the closest?

Activity Sheet 1
A book and a film

Learning Objective: To recognise similarities and differences between the same story in different media.

Name _____ Date _____

Make notes below on any similarities and/or differences between a book and a film version of the book.

	Book	Film
Title		
Characters		
Setting		
Plot		
Events		
Mood		

How is that conveyed on film?

What are their characteristics?

How are they 'described'?

How are these shown?

Is the time or mood changed?

Is the setting the same?

Is the viewpoint the same?

Has the 'narrative' changed?

Have any of the events changed?

Have events been added or dropped?

How was the mood conveyed to the reader/viewer?

What do you think the book does best?

Which one do you prefer? Why?

What do you think the film does best?

FILM NARRATIVE
Brilliant Ideas to Get Boys Writing 9–11 © A & C Black

Activity Sheet 2
Film maker's craft

Learning Objective: To recognise similarities and differences between the same story in different media.

Name _____ **Date** _____

Title of film:
Characters, setting and plot:

Look closely at the film and make a note of the film maker's use of techniques to tell the narrative, using visual effects.

Use of colour and light:

My opinion:

Use of sound:

My opinion:

Viewpoint:

My opinion:

Mood in film:

My opinion:

Did the visual effects help your enjoyment of the narrative?

About a character

Learning Objective: To recognise how film makers build up strong characters.

Name _____ **Date** _____

Choose a character you admire from film, either animation or drama. Discuss your character with a partner. Make notes and then write a description of the character for the actor to play the part or for the artist to draw the animated character.

Character:

How were these conveyed? Mannerisms? Speech? Actions?

Appearance:

Personality and attitudes:

How did costume and make-up help achieve this?

Strengths and weaknesses:

How were these conveyed? Interaction? Actions?

Use your notes to write a description of the character. Display your description beside an image of your character.

Activity Sheet 4
Conversation script

Learning Objective: To recognise the significance of dialogue in unfolding a story.

Name _____ **Date** _____

Watch the film clip, without sound. Make notes as you watch about what you think is going on in the scene. Jot down any ideas you have for the dialogue. How important was the actual dialogue to this scene?

Discuss the scene with your partner and write a brief summary of the scene you have just watched. Include information about the characters and the action.

Write a script for the dialogue which took place in the clip. Include stage directions.

Scene name:

Scene description:

Cast:

Continue the dialogue on the back of the sheet.

Cartoon for Reception class

Learning Objective: To create entertaining characters and an engaging, simple plot.

Name _____ **Date** _____

Plan your cartoon using the prompts on the page. Don't forget to add as much detail as possible. When you have finished your notes, plan your narrative using storyboards.

Character:

Physical description:

> Characteristics
> Mannerisms

Setting:

> Place
> Same setting throughout?
> Time and season

Plot:

Viewpoint:

Visual effects:

Events:

DRAMATIC CONVENTIONS AND PLAYS

Purpose	to entertain, amuse and engage an audience
Structure	usually sequential; written through dialogue, often in more than one scene; acts rather than chapters; set layout, descriptions of characters, setting and stage direction separated
Language features	usually present tense; conversational language; directions use more formal language
Visual features	distinctive layout; sometimes illustrations
Examples	*Fool's Gold*, by David Calcutt; *Time Switch*, by Steve Barlow and Steve Skidmore; *Let's Go to London*, by Kaye Umansky; *Play Time*, by Julia Donaldson; *The Twits: Play for Children*, by Roald Dahl; *Three Plays for Children*, by Oscar Wilde and Phil Clarke

Cross-curricular suggestions

History
★ Choose a variety of exciting historical scenes from the topic being studied and have the children work in groups to put them into dramatic format. They could write a play script – setting the scene, giving stage directions and writing dialogue – and then act out the finished play to the class.

Art
★ Children take figures or a particular scene from a painting and incorporate as the characters or the setting for a new play written in small groups. They could perform this to the class.
★ Create backdrops and props for the play.

Music
★ Use simple percussion instruments for sound effects while performing drama with the class.

Teacher's notes

Use the **Challenge Cards** (Resource Sheet 31) to extend the unit.

Activity Sheet 1

Discuss with children the purpose of plays – to entertain, amuse and engage an audience. Arrange for children to see a play, either in a theatre or on DVD and discuss what they thought of it and how they felt about it. Give them Resource Sheet 28 to review the play. Talk about dramatic texts and how they differ from narrative texts. In small groups, give children a copy of a play text and the narrative text of the same title e.g. *James and the Giant Peach*, *The Twits*. Before they look at the play, ask the children what they think will be the same and what might be different. Ask them to consider the play and note examples on the activity sheet of conventions particular to plays: layout of the text, mainly dialogue with a new line for each new speaker; set and stage directions. Discuss the responses children have written. Ask them what is the same about the play and the book. The narrative, the characters and the plot are basically the same. Back in their groups ask children to look for and discuss the differences between the two, and to note them on the sheet.

Activity Sheet 2

On the whiteboard, display Resource Sheet 29 and discuss what children know about the conventions of plays. Underline the text which tells you the stage setting description and the stage directions. Why are the stage directions important? Ask children to role-play the scene, leaving out the two stage directions: *'Will tried to walk in front of **Prospero**, but **Prospero** turns away.'* and *'Once again, Prospero turns away.'* Does it make a difference? Ask children to play the scene with and without those stage directions for the class and discuss the difference. In groups of three, give the activity sheet to children. Ask them to read the scene description and then to role-play the scene and take notes (recording a fairly finished scene will help them to write it) – the scene should not take longer than a couple of minutes when acted. When they agree on their final scene they write it on the sheet, using the prompts. They then swap scripts and act out each other's scene, as written; then discuss with the script writers how it went – did they have enough information, were the stage directions useful etc?

Activity Sheet 3

Revisit the scene from *Fool's Gold* (Resource Sheet 29) or another play the children are familiar with. Who are the characters in the play? Talk about what you know about each of them, from the text. If you read the whole play would you know more about the characters? In the cast list these three characters are described as: Prospero – a doctor; Miranda – his daughter; Will – Prospero's servant. What details of the characters would it be important to include in the play? And how important is the setting? In *Fool's Gold* the setting for Act One is simply 'A room in Prospero's house.' If you were going to write a play would you want to have more information? Would you need to provide more information to actors who were going to stage the play? These notes are called 'Production notes'

and they include lighting (to show time of day etc.) and sounds (very important for a radio play, but can also give extra information to the audience about when the play is set). Give the activity sheet to pairs of children and ask them to write: character descriptions for two of the characters in the play; the setting and the production notes.

Activity Sheet 4

Activities 4 and 5 help children to plan a play in five acts and then work on each of the acts in more detail, before writing the script. This will take place over time, as children will need time to discuss and try out the scenes, if they are to be useful. Children begin by thinking about the theme for their play, then make a list of possibilities and discuss the pros and cons of each. It could be a traditional tale retold, a story they know and like (one with lots of dialogue is good), or a situation they invent. It will be useful if they are all working on the same theme. Think about the narrative structure of plays and ask children to break the story up into five acts, with a conflict and a resolution. The conflict can be introduced at any point, but it usually comes to a climax toward the end of the play, with the resolution in the final act. Give children the activity sheet, and, in groups, they discuss and plan their play, act by act. Suggest that they create their narrative 'structure' before completing the box on the right hand side of the sheet.

Activity Sheet 5

Using one or two of the scenarios created in the previous activity, ask children to choose an act to plan and write. It doesn't matter if all the acts are not allocated. Give pairs of children the activity sheet and ask them to work on a detailed script for their act, using the sheet for their notes and then drafting the act on a separate sheet of paper. Give children time to role-play their act, as this will help. When they have finished a draft, they ask a friend to review it. Remind children to be constructive in their reviews (Resource Sheet 30 could be used for this, or display a series of questions on the board). After reading the review, children should make the changes and write a finished script accompanied by the cast list, production notes etc. If possible, allow children time to work with other children to present the play to the class, either in real time, or by making a video of their performance. Display the scripts.

REFLECTION & FEEDBACK suggestions

Ask children to reflect on the play they have written, and discuss, with a writing partner, which part of the task they found hardest, and which part easiest. Discuss with the class the differences between a performance for the stage, radio, film or television. How would they have to change their work to move it into a different media?

GETTING STARTED

Role-play

Ask the children to choose a character from television or film which would be well known to the class e.g. *Harry Potter*; *Homer Simpson*; *Superman*; *Luke Skywalker*; *Indiana Jones*; *Peter Parker* … They take on the role of this character completely and face questioning in role as this character from a panel of other children. The answers they give to the panel's questioning will determine how successfully the person has become the character.

Script writing

Children tape a simple conversation (in role) in pairs. They swap it with another pair, listen to the tape and write the conversation as a script.

What happens next?

Find some dramatic pictures from magazines, put them up on the whiteboard then ask children in pairs or small groups to act out 'what happens next'.

Audition

Together choose a small number of characters from a radio or television drama. Ask children to choose a character and prepare an audition as the character. They can bring one prop or piece of clothing to the audition, but they can't dress as the character. Choose a director who will watch the auditions, and choose a person to play each of the characters. If a video recorder is available, tape the auditions.

Make a scene

Ask children to choose a scene from a text or a poem and discuss possible stage directions if it were to become a play. Who would be on stage, what would they be wearing and would they need any props? What would the lighting need to be like? What body language would they need to adopt? They can act out the scene, then write the stage directions.

Snapshot drama

Read out a scene from a text. It could be something the class has already read or something completely new. Stop at a certain point and ask the class to describe this 'freeze frame'. In small groups they make notes on the action at that very moment: what facial expressions do the characters have, what is the mood of the setting, what body language have they adopted? As an extension to this, for a previously unread piece, the children could even work in groups to write the next bit of action.

A play text

Learning Objective: To recognise the special features of a dramatic text, and note differences between that and narrative.

Name _____ **Date** _____

Name of play:	Author:

Examples from text and comments:

Layout of text and dialogue:

Set description:

Stage direction:

Now compare the play and book versions. Make a note of similarities and differences.

Similarities	Differences

Writing a scene

Learning Objective: To focus on the way in which dialogue is written in a dramatic text.

Name _____ **Date** _____

Read the description of this scene. In your group, role-play the scene and make notes so that you can write it as a scene from a play.

Cast list:
Remember to say who the characters are.

Setting description:
Give the detail needed to stage the scene.

Scene:
Remember to include stage directions.
Start each character's speech on a new line, with their name.

Robin Hood and Will Scarlet have stopped a lone traveller in Sherwood Forest, by forcing him off his horse. The traveller is on the ground and they want to know who he is and if he has a purse of gold.

With some friends, think of another scene from a traditional story or one of your stories that you could turn into a short play. Write the descriptive text together.

Characters and setting

Learning Objective: To use dramatic conventions in rewriting a known text as a play.

Name _____ **Date** _____

Characters:
Who are they?
How do you know?

What do they do
in the play?

What characteristics
do they have?

Setting:
Where is it?
Describe it.

Is time and place
important?

Production notes:
How will the setting be shown?
What lighting, sounds and props?

Activity Sheet 4
Planning a play

Learning Objective: To plan the narrative structure of a play, and implement dramatic conventions.

Name _____ **Date** _____

In your group make notes to plan the events in your play. When will you introduce the conflict? When will it be resolved?

Beginning
Act One:

Middle
Act Two:

Act Three:

Act Four:

Ending
Act Five:

Cast list:

Setting:

Production notes:

Props:

Planning the scenes

Learning Objective: To understand the component parts of a dramatic production.

Name _____ **Date** _____

Act _____

Synopsis of act:

Setting:

Production notes:

Costumes:

Action:

Links:
(from previous act, or to next act)

EXTENDING NARRATIVE

Purpose	to entertain and develop interest by extending the narrative not necessarily in a linear way
Structure	often non-sequential events, written in sections or chapters, derived from existing plot, setting and characters; each section or chapter may contain beginning, middle and ending and a problem and resolution
Language features	usually past tense; dialogue and descriptive language; first and third person pronouns
Visual features	may contain illustrations
Examples	*The Hobbit*, by J.R.R. Tolkien; *The Lion, the Witch and the Wardrobe*, by C.S. Lewis; the *Harry Potter* stories, by J.K. Rowling; *His Dark Materials* trilogy, by Philip Pullman; *Jason and the Argonauts*, *King Arthur and the Round Table*

Cross-curricular suggestions

Art and Design
★ Children can use sculpture, collage and other art skills to create a series of backdrops to display in a corridor to accompany the chapters of the quest.

ICT
★ Children can create ICT presentations of their stories to include visual and audio material.

History
★ Children can research figures from quest adventures to explore whether they really existed or are fictional.

Teacher's notes

Use the **Challenge Cards** (Resource Sheet 33) to extend the unit.

Activity Sheet 1

Provide children with a range of titles containing non-linear quests. Encourage them to read and discuss them with a partner or small group. In class, choose one title and highlight its organisation and structure or make notes based on a number of titles, using specific references from the texts. What do children notice about the characters and the setting? Is the quest a linear narrative, or are there 'episodes' through the text? What do they notice about the 'episodes'? They often each have a beginning, middle and ending and a problem and resolution, related to the main quest. Give the activity sheet to small groups of children and ask them to use it to plan and make notes for their quest. Remind children to take time to discuss each section of the plan and to make a list of questions which need to be answered. They can also use other planning devices such as spidergrams and story maps to help them make their decisions. Suggest that they keep a separate list of good words and phrases to use. The quest can be set in the past, the future or the present. The quest can be to find something (or someone), to claim something or to overcome something. Each of the 'episodes' in a quest can include a journey, a battle or a puzzle.

Activity Sheet 2

Before beginning this activity, groups could make a list of characters they know from other quest narratives, with a list of their characteristics e.g. heroes: valiant, brave, strong, wise etc. Children choose their characters; they will need a hero and a villain, but which other characters will they want to have? Is there a narrator or quest guide? Are there comrades to help the hero? Are there any creatures in the quest: are they good or bad creatures? Suggest that children make a list of characteristics for the characters, and a list of the actions they think each character may have to participate in – how does this affect the physical or mental description of the character? Give the activity sheet to groups of children to make notes about their characters. The groups may be split into subgroups with responsibility for character descriptions of different characters. The 'profile' on Resource Sheet 32 could be used for any of their characters.

Activity Sheet 3

Discuss the settings for quest narratives – think about Hogwarts and Narnia. They are often not very different from real settings, but they have some magical qualities. Sometimes they take ordinary objects, e.g. Dr Who's police box, and create another world inside. In a quest there are often a number of different settings. In groups, children think about the settings they would like to have in their quest. Give them the activity sheet and ask them to draw some of the different settings and then describe them using strong adjectives, providing detail of the differences in the setting from the real word and making particular note of 'magical' objects important to the narrative. Further settings can be added and a story 'landscape' mapped out showing the relationship of one setting to another. Children may scan drawings or images into the computer and use an art package to alter and enhance images, then add descriptions and captions to highlight important features in the story.

Activity Sheet 4

Take one of the quest adventures the class have been discussing and map the events or chapters; show that the events are not linear, and could come in any order. In groups, children review the plan they created in the first activity and revise it if necessary. Give the groups the activity sheet, which can be copied to A3 to provide more space for children to make their notes. The sheet can also be cut into separate strips, so that extra 'chapters' can be added. Children collaborate to decide the number of chapters they want in their quest, before ending the quest. Remind them that the order can be changed. They may want to 'trial run' some of their proposed 'challenges' or 'chapters' to be sure they make exciting stages in the quest. Suggest that they keep these role-plays short in duration, so that they can finish the task. Invite them to share their plan with another group, and to transfer their plan to the computer if they wish.

Activity Sheet 5

Working in the same groups as the previous activity, ask children to allocate the writing of chapters among the group, but suggest that they come back together to write the final chapter. Give them the activity sheet to make notes for their chapter and also suggest that they make notes, on the back of the sheet, of strong verbs and adjectives to use. When they have finished their notes, they write their first draft before looking for suitable sound effects on the computer. Ask them to give their draft to a writing partner in their group for review. Resource Sheet 30 can be used by the reviewer, but remind the children to be constructive in their comments. When each child has revised their draft, they can finish it on the computer and add the sound effects. The final chapter can be written together and added to the other chapters for a completed quest adventure, which can be shared, or 'published' on the school web/intranet for other classes to read.

REFLECTION & FEEDBACK suggestions

Discuss the work children put into the quest adventure and ask them what they enjoyed most about the task. Review some of the texts and discuss why they are exciting. Send them to another class and ask for feedback.

Getting Started

Favourite adventure

Make a list of quest adventures on television or electronic games. Ask pairs of children to 'champion' each of the chosen adventures with a video or oral presentation on the school website. Ask everyone to vote on their favourite and see which is the most popular with each age group.

Gripping devices

Select particular passages from a quest narrative e.g. the beginning; a crucial part; a cliffhanging moment … Discuss the language and vocabulary the author has chosen to grip the reader's attention. Can the children identify any devices the writer has used to engage the reader?

Role-play

Put drawings of quest heroes and villains into a hat. Ask children, in pairs, to choose one of each and then to rehearse a role-play between the two characters to present to the class.

Which quest?

Ask pairs of children to draw the main character and the setting from a quest adventure they are familiar with. Ask them to challenge another pair to guess the storyline from clues in the drawing.

Reverse role

Using the same quest heroes and villains ask pairs of children to tell the tale from their point of view and record it. Ask the class to listen to the pairs of recordings and to vote on which point of view they prefer; ask some children to justify their decisions.

Greek quests

Give a number of 'popular' Greek quests such as *Jason and the Golden Fleece*, *Perseus and Medusa* to children and ask them to explore the similarities and differences. Make a display for the library. This could tie in with a History topic on Ancient Greece.

Planning a quest

Learning Objective: To plan and create the structure of a quest adventure.

Name _____ **Date** _____

Discuss each of these features of your quest with your group and make notes in the boxes below.

The setting
The time and the place.
Are there different settings?
Where are they?

The characters
Who is the hero?
Who is the villain?
Is there a narrator/guide?
Does the hero have helpers?
Are there other creatures?

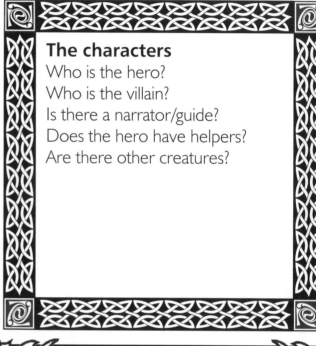

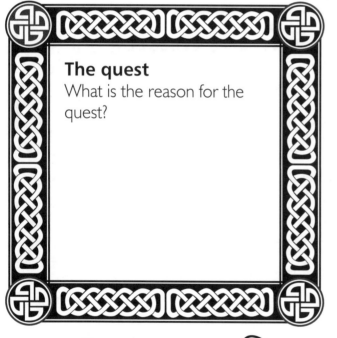

The quest
What is the reason for the quest?

Objects to help
Are there any objects to help?

The challenges
What challenges are faced during the quest?

The resolution
Is the quest successful?

Press to go forward or backward in time.

Activity Sheet 2
Quest characters

Learning Objective: To choose and plan characters for a quest adventure.

Name _____ Date _____

Make notes about each of your characters in the boxes. Draw a portrait of each character and write a profile to accompany the portrait on separate sheets.

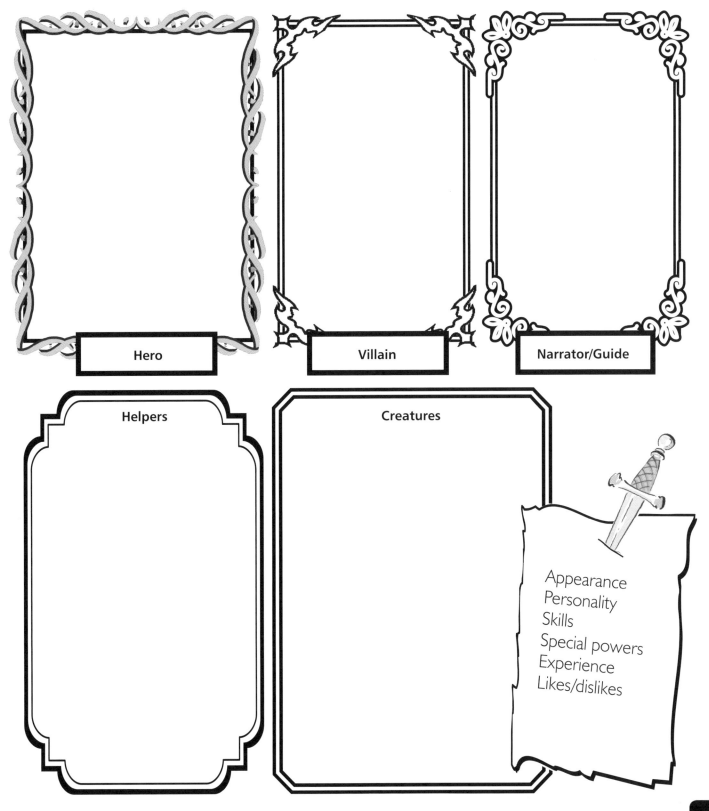

Hero

Villain

Narrator/Guide

Helpers

Creatures

Appearance
Personality
Skills
Special powers
Experience
Likes/dislikes

Activity Sheet 3
Quest settings

Learning Objective: To choose and plan settings for a quest adventure.

Name _____ **Date** _____

Draw the settings for your quest on the left side of each box. Make notes about each setting beside it. Make sure you highlight any magical or important objects or places which are 'not what they seem'.

Setting 1

Setting 2

Setting 3

EXTENDING NARRATIVE
Brilliant Ideas to Get Boys Writing 9–11 © A & C Black

The problems of a quest

Learning Objective: To plan challenges faced by the hero in the quest.

Name _____ **Date** _____

What challenges are faced by your hero in the quest? Does the hero face the villain in each challenge? When does the hero need help, or use the magical objects? Make each challenge exciting. You can add extra challenges. Does the hero succeed in the end?

Where does the hero begin the journey? Who does the hero meet?	*Is this challenge in a new setting? Does the hero meet the villain? Is there a stand-off?*
Is the next challenge more difficult? Does the hero need help? How does the hero escape?	*How does the hero face another obstacle? Is it the same villain, or a new one? How does the hero feel?*
Does the hero face the villain at the end of the quest? Does the hero have a secret weapon? Does the hero triumph?	

Plan your chapter

Learning Objective: To plan a chapter in detail and to suggest appropriate software to produce a multi-modal text.

Name _____ **Date** _____

Use the prompts to make notes for your chapter in the quest adventure. Suggest sound effects to accompany the chapter.

> *Use the chapter opening to set the scene, introduce the hero again and any new characters.*

> *What does the hero see, hear, smell and feel? How is the hero moving through the scene? Who does the hero meet? How does he act?*

> *What happens next? What does the hero have to do? Is there a battle, or a chase? Keep the reader guessing!*

> *How does the chapter end? Is there a winner and a loser? Does the quest go on? Can you keep the reader waiting for the next chapter?*

★ Look on the internet for possible sound effects for the problems encountered as the hero travels.

★ Draft your chapter and ask a friend to review your draft. When you have a finished version, type the text into a computer program and attach a sound track.

SHORT STORIES WITH FLASHBACKS

Purpose	to amuse, entertain and interest; sometimes to inform
Structure	opening or orientation; a series of events and/or a complication and resolution
Language features	usually past tense; descriptive language and vocabulary (adjectives, strong verbs); sometimes dialogue; first and third person pronouns
Visual features	may include illustrations, including maps and narrative reference; some cartoon format (e.g. Manga)
Examples	*Shadow Puppet*, by Jane Clarke; *Dark Eagle*, by Neil Tonge; *Space Pirates*, by Tony Bradman; *My Kind of School*, ed by Tony Bradman; *Chasing the Sun*: *Stories from Africa*, selected by Veronique Tadjo; *Mission to Marathon*, by Geoffrey Trease; *A Candle in the Dark*, by Adele Geras

Cross-curricular suggestions

Drama
★ Children turn a short story into a small production to present to others.

History
★ Children use a historical period being studied as the setting for a short story with a flashback to provide additional detail. They should use authentic details.

Music
★ Children use a piece of music as inspiration for the setting of a short story.

Use the **Challenge Cards** (Resource Sheet 36) to extend the unit.

Teacher's notes

Activity Sheet 1

Ask children if they can think of any story, film or television programme which uses flashback techniques. Make a list and determine in each case why the flashback was used – usually to give information from the past. Sometimes the flashback goes to another time and place, for instance in *Harry Potter and the Chamber of Secrets*, the scenes with Tom Riddle are from an earlier time. Give the activity sheet to pairs of children and ask them to discuss the scenarios, choose one and add a flashback. Suggest that they tell the tale to each other first, using lots of different ways to introduce the flashback. They should make notes on the sheet of the different possibilities of language which link the flashback to the tale. When they have drafted their story with flashback, ask them to record it using a device such as music or a sound to signal the flashback.

Activity Sheet 2

Explain that there is not much time in a short story to gradually develop characters. A detailed picture must be painted quite quickly in this genre. Display the scenarios on Resource Sheet 34 and ask children to choose one with a writing partner. Give them time to discuss the scenarios and make notes on how they would use them in a short story, and what flashback would help. They may role-play some possible events and decide whose point of view the story will be told from, before making notes. Suggest they try a number of different flashbacks – to another time, another place, earlier in the day or year etc. Suggest that rather than use the first one they think of they should try to find a flashback which will add something to the story. Remind them to think of an interesting trigger for the flashback and to make a list of possible links to it. In a plenary session, ask children to tell the class what language they used to link to their flashback and compile a class list.

Activity Sheet 3

Display Resource Sheet 35 and ask children to write a flashback based on the text. They may tell their flashback in the first or the third person, by either taking on the role of the character, or telling their story. As both scenarios are from the past, remind children to use historically accurate detail when possible. Give out the activity sheet and ask children to consider how they will write the flashback to tell the reader about the early life of the characters, and how they came to be in this situation. With their writing partner they can discuss various possibilities before making their notes on the sheet. If a class list of possible linking phrases has been compiled, provide it for the children. If not, discuss possibilities with the class.

Activity Sheet 4

In this activity children plan a story, with flashback, which they will turn into a visual text in the next activity. Remind children that the narrative structure remains the same and they should look for strong verbs and adjectives to describe the characters, settings and atmosphere. They should consider where in the story the flashback will appear, at the beginning to give the reader additional information or later when an event or an object (with magical properties) provides drama. Also remind children that in a short story they need to grip their readers quickly, and not include incidental information.

Activity Sheet 5

Using the narrative they have prepared in the previous activity, children now draw or write their frames in the order they intend to deliver them to the audience; this might not be in time order. They add notes to indicate how they will move from frame to frame and what music or camera techniques will accompany each of the frames. Like other narratives, they need to work on their draft. Suggest that when they have created their first draft that they discuss it with friends and get their feedback before proceeding to a second, more detailed draft and ultimately to either a visual text (a cartoon or picture book) or to a PowerPoint presentation or short video presentation.

REFLECTION & FEEDBACK suggestions

Review the presentations created by children, and ask classmates to give constructive feedback. Show a film or television programme which uses the flashback technique and ask the children if they now have a better understanding of the techniques used.

GETTING STARTED

Flashback in print

Give groups the task of finding flashbacks in print. Suggest that they talk to the school librarian and to the town librarian for help in sourcing lots of examples.

Flashback

Give children a character from fiction and ask them to think of a possible flashback. Ask them to script and act out the flashback and record the presentation. Compare the different scenarios created for the same characters.

Put it together

Give the class three or four characters e.g. a 14-year-old on holiday, a dog, a life guard and a magic surfboard. In groups of four, each person is given the job of writing a scenario for the four characters. They then swap scenarios and each group writes a flashback for another group's scenario. They swap back and evaluate the flashback written by the other group for their original scenario.

Back to the past

In groups, make a list of possible magical objects (like portal keys) which would take you back to a particular time in the past. See how many you can come up with.

Flashback poll

Ask children to create a questionnaire asking pupils at the school to give them the names of films or television series which use the flashback technique. Once they have a comprehensive list, make a school poll to find out which is the most popular.

Activity Sheet 1
Adding a flashback

Learning Objective: To add a flashback to an existing tale.

Name _____ Date _____

Choose one of these tales and add a flashback, to give the reader information about events in the past.

As the bells rang all over the kingdom, Arthur was preparing himself for his coronation. He had been awake most of the night, thinking about the responsibilities which lay ahead of him. After the early service in the chapel, he had broken his fast alone.

Would Arthur remember pulling Excalibur from the stone?

King Beowulf now rules the Land of the Greats. He has grown old, his hair has turned silver-grey, like wolf fur. Often as he sat by the fire in the evening one of the young boys in the camp would come quietly to his side, and touch the long scar on his face.

Did this make Beowulf think of how he came by the scar?

What device will you use to link the flashback to the tale – a piece of music or a sound?

How will you link to the flashback?

How will you link back to the story?

Flashback ideas

Learning objective: To use a flashback to provide information about what has gone before, not explicitly explained in the text.

Name _____ Date _____

Choose one of the scenario cards, giving characters and situations. With a writing partner, use the scenario to begin a short story. Make notes on the sheet for your story, including a flashback.

Characters and situation:
What do you think the characters are doing in this situation?
What is going to happen in the story?
How could a flashback provide more information to make the situation clearer to the reader?
Make notes about the trigger for the flashback, and how you will link it to the story.

Activity Sheet 3
A happier time

Learning Objective: To use a flashback to give personal details.

Name _____ Date _____

Read the two short story beginnings on Resource Sheet 35 and talk about the characters with your writing partner. How did the characters come to be in these positions? Use the flashback to give the reader information about how they came to be here.

Story:
Trigger to flashback:
What information will the flashback provide?
How will this help the reader?
Link to flashback
Flashback
Link back to story

Remember to give details to the reader.

Remember to provide detail of the time and place.

Activity Sheet 4
Short story

Learning Objective: To plan a short story, including a flashback.

Name _____ **Date** _____

With a writing partner, choose a topic for a short story. Use this sheet to make the notes for your story.

Title:

Characters:
How many?
Appearance?
Personality?
How will you introduce them?

Setting:
Where and when?
See, hear, smell, and feel?
How will you introduce it?

Atmosphere:
What is the mood?
How do you tell the reader?

Plot:
What happens?

Problem and resolution:
What is the complication?
How is it resolved?

Flashback:
What is the trigger? – magical? informational?
To another time or place?
How will you link it?
How does it fit in the story?

Activity Sheet 5
Storyboard

Learning Objective: To storyboard a short story, in preparation for creating a visual text.

Name _____ **Date** _____

Draw or write the main scenes in your short story on the storyboard. Write your notes for making it a visual text below each frame. Make a note of how you will link to the flashback.

Flashback

Have you got a great opening?

Don't forget to end on a high!

POETRY

Purpose	to entertain and give pleasure; to puzzle and appeal to emotions; to convey messages, concepts, moods and stories.
Structure	various, according to the purpose of the poet
Language features	carefully chosen words; devices such as: rhythm, rhyme, alliteration, onomatopoeia, repetition, metaphor, simile, personification
Visual features	some forms have visual representation – concrete and acrostic poems and calligrams
Examples	rhyme, ballad, limerick, free verse, narrative poems, haiku, cinquain, acrostic, concrete

Cross-curricular suggestions

Music
★ Children use instruments to accompany and enhance the reading of poems.
★ Find the rhythm in some poems and ask children to tap or clap the rhythm as backing to the poem as it is read.
★ Use a piece of music to inspire the children to write a poem, in response.

Literacy
★ Agree a class definition of a simile – when one object is compared with another object – and make a class collection of similes for children to use e.g. as mad as a hatter; as blind as a bat.

Art
★ Ask children to respond to poems in art classes, using a variety of media.

Use the **Challenge Cards** (Resource Sheet 40) to extend the unit.

Activity Sheet 1

Spend some time looking at examples of poems and discuss the purpose of poetry. Why do children think poets write poems and what do they think about poems, including how poems make them feel? Ask children if they know any of the language features (devices) used by poets. Display Resource Sheet 37 and look at each of these forms. Divide the class into groups and ask each group to find some examples of one of the forms. Make a display of the different forms in the classroom. Display the activity sheet and discuss some of the devices listed; what examples can they find of the device and what poems can they find which use the device? (Resource Sheet 38 has some examples of rhyme.) Give the sheet to children in pairs or groups and ask them to research each of the devices – giving examples and noting the poems in which each device is found. Encourage children to tell their partner which form they like best, and why. Children can then join with another pair or group and compare their findings. Children then prepare a poem to recite – alone or with a partner, and, in a plenary session, ask some children to recite their examples.

Activity Sheet 2

At the beginning of the activity, remind children of the work they did in the previous activity, looking at metaphors, similes and personification. Suggest that children work in pairs to revisit poetry books and create their own examples of metaphors, similes and personification.

Activity Sheet 3

Introduce some examples of 'free verse' and ask children what they think the features of these poems might be: they don't necessarily rhyme and they often have a different written appearance from other poetry. But do they use similes, metaphors, personification or other devices? Children find one or two free verse poems and look at them in detail with a partner. (Poems on Resource Sheet 39 can be used.) Then ask children to think about a topic they would like to write a poem about. A list of possible subjects could be compiled together, then displayed. Subjects could range from a person (friend, fantasy character), an animal (real or imagined), a feeling (excitement, loneliness), an object or another poem used as a model. Display the activity sheet and discuss the prompts. Give the sheet to children and

encourage them to work together to think and talk about what they want to write about and the type of poem they want to write. They should collect lots of words before they start; and see the first draft as a starting point. Give them time to work through the stages to a finished poem.

Activity Sheet 4

Look at and read some examples of concrete or shape poetry, give the children time to find other examples and to find one they like. (Robert Froman's *Hot enough to see* is an interesting example.) Encourage them to discuss their choice for a concrete poem with a partner (it does not have to be one of the subjects on the sheet). Give the activity sheet to children and encourage them to write words and phrases or whole sentences about the particular subject they have chosen. They should try to use imagery in the form of metaphor, simile or personification to make their ideas even more vivid, if appropriate to shape. They arrange these on the page to suggest an image of the subject of the poem. Some children may find it easier to begin with a graphic outline into which they write their words. When they have drafted, reviewed and polished their poems, ask children to scan their poems into the computer and make a PowerPoint display of the class poems. Look through the display together and ask some children for their comments.

REFLECTION & FEEDBACK suggestions

Ask children, in pairs or groups, to choose a poet (either one they have been studying or one they have 'discovered') and to investigate what is distinctive about the style or the content of their poems. In a plenary session ask groups to discuss what they have found with the class. This could lead to a 'poet's corner' display which includes poems by chosen poets, descriptions of their style and information about their works accompanied by recitations of their work recorded for others to listen to.

GETTING STARTED

Theme poems

Children choose a selection of poems of different types related to the same theme e.g. the sea, space, summer… (emphasis on different 'types' of poems). Ask the children to create a visual response e.g. a poster, a painting or collage to decorate the area of the classroom which will display these works.

Poetry group

Set up a display of poems and anthologies for the children to read, including poems and poets from other cultures. Later, divide the class into groups and ask children to bring to the group a copy of their favourite poem to share and discuss together. Ask for a few volunteers to present their choice to the whole class.

My favourite poem

Over a period of time ask children to decide on their favourite poem. Instigate a class vote and find a class favourite. Discuss the reasons why they thought their choice was a good one. Send 'readers' around the school to read a selection of poems to other classes and aim to find a 'School Favourite'.

Dramatic poetry

Children read out a narrative poem, a ballad or a longer poem. Divide the class into small groups and ask them to turn the poem into a play to perform to another class.

Poetic words

Set up sheets of paper (or pages on the class website) where the children can record interesting words, onomatopoeic words, nonsense words, examples of rhyme, metaphor etc. whenever they come across them to use later in writing poetry.

Nonsense words

Find (or draw) a 'nonsense' desk; scan the illustration and put it on the class website. Ask children to add nonsense words to the desk throughout the week. At the end of the week, display the desk and discuss the words.

☆ What ☆ do you think?

Read to the class a selection of different poems over a period of time. Discuss some (but not all) of the poems and ask for comments and responses (feelings).

Poet's devices

Learning Objective: To identify language devices used in poetry.

Name _____ Date _____

Think about each of the devices and find your own examples of each. Write them in the boxes.

Rhyme
A device used in many poems, but by no means all. Words at the end of certain lines rhyme to create a rhythm and pattern.

Onomatopoeia
A word, or words, which sound like the action described by them, such as crunchy crusts.

Similes
When one object is compared with another, usually using 'like' or 'as', e.g. *As blind as a bat.*

Alliteration
Words with the same initial letter, grouped together to form a word picture, e.g. *The slithery snake slipped through the sunshine.*

Repetition
Repeated use of a word or a phrase within a poem, for effect.

Metaphors
When one object is referred to or described as something else, e.g. *He is a loose cannon.*

Personification
When a non-living object is described using human characteristics, e.g. *The branches of the tree reached out to us.*

Activity Sheet 1
Rich images

Learning Objective: To learn and use devices such as metaphor, simile and personification.

Name _____ **Date** _____

With your writing partner, discuss imagery for the subjects below. Try to come up with an example of metaphor, simile and personification for each subject below.

SEA   The sea was a raging animal *(metaphor)*
The sea was as frothy as a child's bath *(simile)*
The sea whispered quietly *(personification)*

	Metaphor	Simile	Personification
A candle			
A dragon			
A fire			
A drum			
A mouse			
A snake			
A tree			
A mountain			
Rain			
Wind			
A storm			
Water			

Can you use some of your examples in a joint poem?

Brilliant Ideas to Get Boys Writing 9–11 © A & C Black

Free verse

Learning Objective: To choose a topic and to draft and write a poem.

Name _____ Date _____

What will your poem be about?

What will you title your poem?

Words you can use.

Draft copy of poem.

★ Read your draft aloud.
★ Make changes.
★ Discuss with a friend.
★ Improve your poem.

Brilliant Ideas to Get Boys Writing 9–11 © A & C Black

Create concrete poems

Learning Objective: To look at a range of poetry types, choose one and innovate on it.

Name _____ **Date** _____

Choose a subject for a concrete poem. Discuss words, phrases and imagery conjured up by this subject with your writing partner. Make notes as you go along and together select the best ones to use. Now arrange your ideas on the page in a way that suggests an image of your subject

The sea
Snow
A rocket
A plane
A car
Fireworks

A snake
An elephant
A storm
A parachute
Our house
A kite

NON-FICTION

Most writing in the real world combines several text types. However, separating out the 'pure' text types and structures, explicitly naming their individual features can help children gain a better understanding. Explain and use these features and encourage boys to use them in their own writing.

★ Share books which appeal to boys and provide opportunities to respond to them – role-play, dramatisation etc.

★ Share books which appeal to boys and provide opportunities to respond to them, using a range of media, including electronic.

★ Create a bank of relevant vocabulary, phrases and prompts which help thinking, planning and reviewing.

★ Use *Talk for writing* principles and provide lots of opportunity to talk and collaborate prior to and throughout the writing process.

★ Display, demonstrate and discuss model texts and visuals and give a clear purpose for each task.

★ Ensure children discuss and agree text purpose and audience.

★ Provide questions for planning and a range of 'frames' for use.

★ Make available a range of tools, including ICT tools.

★ Display work in progress and finished work, in different versions.

★ Ensure opportunities for review and reflection are available and provide effective feedback.

INSTRUCTIONS

Purpose	to describe how to do or make something or direct someone
Structure	statement of goal or purpose; list of materials required; series of steps in order (can include alternatives); statement of outcome
Language features	action verbs – imperative; specialist vocabulary; present tense; time conjunctions to indicate order; adverbs
Visual features	bullet points or numbered steps; illustrations, photos and diagrams to support text, often including image of the final product
Examples	recipes; science experiments; craft instructions; games rules; directions; instructions and instruction manuals; safety leaflets

Cross-curricular suggestions

History
★ Children write a set of instructions for something outrageous from the period of history you are studying such as 'How to make a bomb detector' or 'How to mummify a pharaoh'.

Science
★ Children write a set of instructions to accompany a science experiment.

DT
★ Children write a set of instructions for a construction project.

Teacher's notes

Use the **Challenge Cards** (Resource Sheet 44) to extend the unit.

Activity Sheet 1

Discuss the different types of instructions we use and what the purpose is of each. Ask children what instructions they have used recently and why – make a list on the whiteboard. Display the activity sheet and discuss the column which has been completed, and then ask children in pairs to complete the remaining columns and to find examples of each type of instruction text. Then ask the pairs to reflect on one example of instruction text, using General Reference Sheet 'Text Explorer'. Ask them to scan the text and add the appropriate labels from Resource Sheet 41. Display all the labelled texts and discuss the features which have been revealed.

Activity Sheet 2

Ask groups of children to discuss a simple recipe they know how to cook. Can they order their thoughts and give the instructions orally – listing ingredients and utensils and then describing the process step-by-step, noting any safety information? Others in the group can transcribe on a flip chart. Discuss one of these examples with the class, highlighting time connectives, imperative verbs and the other structures discussed in the last activity. Give the activity sheet to pairs of children and ask them to discuss the instructions for preparing scrambled eggs. Suggest they role-play the instructions first, and then draw the step-by-step instructions in the flow chart, before writing them on the sheet. Provide at least one recipe from a published source which the children can use to compare with theirs, including the command verbs and time connectives as well as the steps in the process. If time permits, watch a cookery programme then ask children to write a script for a television presentation using their recipe. Give children the opportunity to role-play prior to writing the script and to video their performance.

Activity Sheet 3

Ask the children to describe their journeys to school to a partner, adding as much detail as possible about landmarks etc. Then ask pairs to give a short set of directions to each other – three or four directions only – but not say where the directions are leading to. Can the partner say where the directions will take them? Give the activity sheet to the writing pairs and ask them to look carefully at the map of Ben's route to school (walking). Ask them to write down some good words to use when giving or writing directions. They then write the directions on the sheet and check on the map to see if they are correct. When they have completed the instructions and checked them, ask them to describe how they would change the directions if Ben was going to school by car.

Activity Sheet 4

Discuss with the children the need to be precise when giving instructions, to make them as straightforward as possible for people to follow. Talk about how graphics can be developed and improved upon by including a few words of simple text. Again focus on choosing appropriate vocabulary. Tell children that they are going to write a set of instructions for the children in Year 2. What difference might that make to their instructions? Display Resource Sheet 43 and discuss the prompts on the frame. Then display the two possible instruction challenges on Resource Sheet 44 and ask writing pairs to decide which one they are going to write for Year 2. Remind them to add details which are not provided and decide on the visual text which might help Year 2 children. Using the activity sheet they write a draft of their instructions text. Ask them to swap instructions and write or give an oral review. (Resource Sheet 30 could be used for a written review.) They should then polish their instructions, add the visual text and give them to Year 2, if possible use computer skills to create an integrated text.

Activity Sheet 5

Look around the school at various safety instructions such as how to use a fire extinguisher, or at the instructions in a public place such as how to evacuate in the event of a fire. Together, make a list of safety instructions that could be useful in school. Explain that these should be no more than six to eight steps and that they should be pictorial only, so that those who do not speak English can also follow them. Give children the opportunity to study various safety instructions so that they can use the information provided, or use them as a model. Give pairs or small groups the activity sheet and ask them to first make a note of the purpose of the instructions, the audience and the form they will take. They can then draft their visual instructions. At this point it will probably be useful to have captions or labels on the illustrations, to help refine them. Ask them to discuss their drafts with another adult in the school, and ask for suggestions, before revising their work. Create finished work using art packages on the computer.

REFLECTION & FEEDBACK suggestions

Ask Year 2 children to report back on how easy/difficult the instructions from activity 4 were to follow. The children could consider then how they could make the wording or the pictures clearer.

GETTING STARTED

Collecting evidence

Gather examples from around the school to demonstrate the relevance of certain instructions to the children e.g. fire alarm instructions. Equip them in pairs with a camera to go round the school and playground to gather photographic evidence of any instructions they can find. Provide a time limit of 15 minutes per pair.

Role-play

In groups, children pretend they are on a desert island. What would they have to do – create shelter, start a fire, find and cook food, build a raft? The group should decide on one task and write instructions for the task. They should role-play the situation first and then review to ensure they have included all the steps required.

What did you say?

Put the characters and instructions on Resource Sheet 45 into two hats. Ask children to pick one of each and then, in the role of the characters, give the instructions. There will be some funny role-play scenarios!

What does it mean?

Ask the children to work in pairs to invent a set of self-explanatory visual instructions. Show each one to the class. Can the children tell what it means?

Make a list

Make a list of visual instructions which need no text e.g. the emergency exit running man, symbols for male/female toilets, no smoking, and so on in school and in the community.

Activity Sheet 1
Types of instruction

Learning Objective: To understand the structures and features of different types of instruction.

Name _____ Date _____

Look at the different texts which give instructions and complete the table.

	Directions	Recipe	Game instructions	'How to' instructions	Instruction manual
Purpose	To tell someone how to get from place to place				
Form	note				
Headings	none				
Written text	● no numbers ● time connectives ● imperative verbs e.g. 'go'				
Visuals	● simple map ● arrows				
Example	how to get to a friend's house				

INSTRUCTIONS
Brilliant Ideas to Get Boys Writing 9–11 © A & C Black

Activity Sheet 2

Scrambled eggs

Learning Objective: To use a flow chart to give clear, simple instructions.

Name _____ **Date** _____

Write a set of instructions for preparing scrambled eggs on toast. Illustrate your flow chart first, and then write the instructions. Think about using commanding verbs and clear time connectives.

Ingredients

Method

| 1 | 2 |

| 3 | 4 |

Utensils

| 5 | 6 |

Safety

Activity Sheet 3
Find a route

Learning Objective: To use appropriate connectives when giving directions for travel.

Name _____ Date _____

Ben has moved into 7 Vicarage Lane. Write clear instructions for his route to his new school; include landmarks which will help him. List the words you could use in giving directions.

KEY

- country park
- shops
- golf course
- road
- zebra crossing
- traffic lights
- church
- path

School

School Road

Cross Street

Duck pond

Tennis courts

Vicarage Lane

6 4 2

7 5 3 1

X

London Road

1. Come out of Ben's house. Turn left.
2. _____
3. _____
4. _____
5. _____
6. _____
7. _____

Direction words

INSTRUCTIONS
Brilliant Ideas to Get Boys Writing 9–11 © A & C Black

Instructions for Year 2

Learning Objective: To write instructions for a specific audience.

Name _____ **Date** _____

Make notes and write your draft instructions on the sheet. Review your draft with a writing partner, and then write finished instructions with visual text.

How to:

You will need:

Method:

Safety information:

Visual text:

Activity Sheet 5

Safety instructions

Learning Objective: To provide instructions as a visual text.

Name _____ Date _____

With a partner write notes about your safety instructions. Draw the sequence of instructions, using the back of the sheet if necessary, in draft.

Purpose of instruction:
Audience:
Form:
You will need:

1	2	3
4	5	6

RECOUNTS

Purpose	to describe an event or experience that has happened in the past; recounts can be personal, factual or imaginative
Structure	opening (orientation) sets the scene, followed by a sequence of events in chronological order and a closing statement
Language features	past tense verbs; first or third person voice; temporal or time connectives; evaluative or personal statements (opinions)
Visual features	photographs; illustrations; diagrams; maps and timelines
Examples	letters, journals, diary; newspaper article; biography and autobiography

Cross-curricular suggestions

Geography
★ Children write a recount of a geography field trip including maps and diagrams.

DT/Science
★ Recounts of experiments in science or creating objects in D&T can be written up afterwards as a recount.

History
★ Recounts of the life of people from another time studied in history can be written as recounts.

Use the **Challenge Cards** (Resource Sheet 48) to extend the unit.

Activity Sheet 1

Ask children to recount something which has happened at school or at home recently. When they have finished, draw attention to the 'who, what, when, where, why' and the events listed in the recount. Explain that when writing a recount it is important to set the scene by introducing 'who, what, when, where, why and how' in the orientation, then listing the events, before finishing with a comment. In a shared session, write a collaborative recount; draw attention to the time connectives, past tense and the use of pronouns. Make a class list of useful words – to introduce the first event: in the beginning, firstly, to start with, on (day or date); to introduce subsequent events: then, next, after that, secondly, thirdly etc; to introduce the final event: in the end, finally, lastly. Review the list of connectives on Resource Sheet 7. Explain that usually only significant events are recalled, generally in the order in which they occurred. Talk about the need for a conclusion or finishing statement. Provide pairs with the activity sheet and ask them to discuss and then make notes for a personal recount which happened at school, using the first person. Display and discuss some of the notes at the end of the session and ask children to write a recount to share with their writing partner.

Note: Resource Sheet 46 has a list of possible recount titles for children to use if necessary.

Activity Sheet 2

Ask the children to recount a series of events from their holidays to a partner. They may wish to create a storyboard of the events to jog their memory and to ensure they get the events in the right sequence. If time permits give them opportunities to do a 'piece to camera' for a holiday programme. Recap on the structure of a recount and the list of time connectives, which are the same in any media. Give the activity sheet to pairs of children and talk about using a journal form to write a recount – particular to personal recounts. Ask children what they think might go in the orientation of a journal – e.g. whose journal it is, when and where it is being written and why – to record events. If a copy of Pepys' diary is in the library, read the entry about the burning of London. Once children have had time to discuss the events, and to draft an orientation, they can write a first draft of their holiday journal on the sheet. Some children could write a postcard recount if they prefer. Display the 'Making it better' and 'Proof-reading' General Reference Sheets and ask children to mark up their draft with improvements (using different coloured pens). Display finished journal entries.

Activity Sheet 3

Look on the internet at some of the events at the Beijing Olympics, particularly at any of the online diaries from Olympians the children might know. Make a list of the things you would need to know if you were going to write a recount of a visit to the Olympics; when would your recount start (the journey out or arrival in Beijing); what are the main events etc. Give children time to conduct some research, and ask them to use the activity sheet to make a timeline of events with a partner. Then suggest they draft an opening or orientation (using the questions they have used before) and then make a list of the events they want to include, before drafting a closing. Suggest they use an online diary format to write their draft, then save and review it with their writing partner before writing a polished diary. If possible suggest they add photos from a clip bank to the diary.

Activity Sheet 4

Begin by reviewing a factual recount from a newspaper. On the whiteboard highlight the orientation, the events in chronological order, the time connectives, the past tense and the conclusion. Children then work in small groups or pairs to find the photo from a news story. They can use one of the photos on Resource Sheet 47 or one from another source. They discuss the story suggested by the photo, thinking and making notes about the orientation and the sequence of events. They then write draft paragraphs on the activity sheet. When they have reviewed their draft, they could write the recount on the computer in a newspaper frame, and if possible add a relevant photo (and caption). Print the newspaper pages, and make a display in the hall with actual newspaper recounts.

Activity Sheet 5

Together talk about possibilities for an imaginary recount: it could be set in a historical period you are studying or it could be an imaginary adventure – to track a Polar Bear – or a fantasy adventure – an expedition into space. In small groups, children explore one or two ideas for an imaginary recount. Encourage them to make notes on all their ideas, and come to a conclusion on the one to pursue. They then make notes about who is involved, where and when it is, what happens and why – just like other recounts. Suggest they use the frames used in earlier activities to make notes, and to write down all the information they might need. They then choose a person from the historical time or on the adventure and write a letter to a friend, describing the events as a recount. Before they start they could make a list of possible paragraph openings – for the orientation: 'I am writing to tell you, You will be interested to hear'; for the events: the time connectives they have been using; for the conclusion: 'It was such …; You would have enjoyed …' Children write their first draft on the activity sheet, but then review and revise it

REFLECTION & FEEDBACK suggestions

Invite children to say which type of recount they found easiest or most enjoyable to write and why. Allow time for children to swap and review each others' work and discuss possible improvements, prior to making finished versions.

GETTING STARTED

When I was …

Ask children to take digital photos of an event in their lives. The photos are then put onto the computer in a timeline and a short recount text is attached for others to read.

Good words

Display some recounts in the classroom, giving the class a chance to read through them in small groups. Discuss the orientation, the manner in which events are recorded i.e. in chronological order, and the closing statement. Ask the groups to make a list of action verbs and time connectives in the recounts and add the list to the display.

Logs and diaries

Make a collection of factual and fictional logs and diaries, for the children to read and enjoy, including the actual logs of Columbus, Cook and Darwin (*The Beagle's Log*) or the fictional Captain's Log from *Star Trek*.

Sporting hero

Make a collection of reports from different local or national sporting events. In pairs, children choose one of the reports. One child becomes the reporter and the other the interviewee who was a participant in the event. Give them 10 minutes to prepare and then five minutes to conduct (and record – video or audio) the interview.

Here is the news

Ask children to choose a reported event from the news. They then become the person involved in the event and recount their version of the event to a partner. Then role-play a news programme with news from the class or school, to camera.

School recount

Learning Objective: To focus on the structure of a recount.

Name _____ Date _____

Choose a recent event from school and make notes for each part of your recount in the boxes. Remember to use the first person.

Orientation				
Who	What	When	Where	Why/How

Events
1
2
3
4

Conclusion
(opinions and feelings)

Activity Sheet 2
Holiday journal

Learning Objective: To write a personal recount in the form of a diary.

Name _____ **Date** _____

Think about what happened in the holidays. Draw a storyboard of the main events you want to write about in your journal, and arrange the events in order. Make a note of the funny things that happened and the things people said, so that you can include them. Begin the journal with an orientation and finish it with a comment about the holidays.

This is the journal of:

Date:

Activity Sheet 3
Beijing Diary

Learning Objective: To plan a factual recount, including a timeline.

Research the information you will need to write a recount of the Beijing Olympics as a diary. Use the timeline to write down the important events, in date order. Write a strong draft opening and closing paragraph on the back of the sheet.

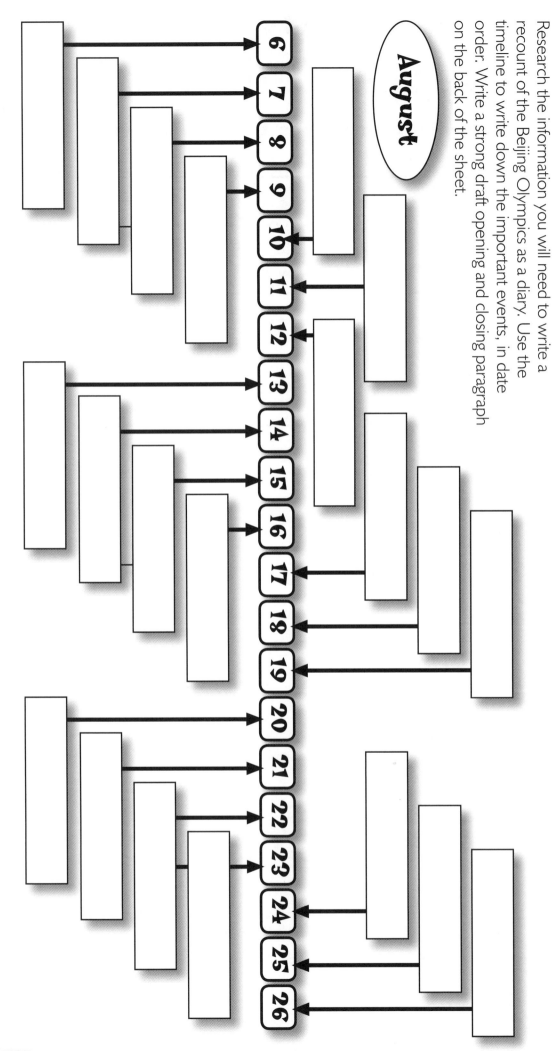

August

6 7 8 9 10 11 12 13 14 15 16 17 18 19 20 21 22 23 24 25 26

RECOUNTS
Brilliant Ideas to Get Boys Writing 9–11 © A & C Black

Read All About It!!

Learning Objective: To recount an item of news and present it as a newspaper article.

Name _____ Date _____

Choose a news photo and plan a recount to accompany it for a newspaper article. Look at some recent newspaper articles before you start.

Title:

Orientation:
What is the recount about – who, what, where, when and why?

Events in time order:
Each event is important.

-
-
-
-
-

Conclusion:
Summary of what happened, and what you think or feel.

Imaginary recount

Learning Objective: To recount an imagined event as a letter.

Name _____ Date _____

Plan your letter about an imaginary series of events and write a draft on the page. When you have reviewed and revised your draft, write the letter on the computer.

Address

Date

Greeting

Orientation

Events

Conclusion

Sign off

PERSUASION

Purpose	to persuade others to accept a point of view, change an attitude or act in a particular way; to promote something
Structure	opening statement of the issue; sequenced points to support opinion, usually supported by evidence; carefully selected facts; concluding statement or summary
Language features	imperative command verbs; present tense; time connectives and conjunctions; specialist vocabulary; sometimes passive voice; emotional language
Visual features	photos; illustrations; charts and graphs
Examples	letters; advertisements; brochures; posters; e-mails; newspapers; radio and television; magazine features

Cross-curricular suggestions

Science/Art
★ Children create a poster to persuade people to eat healthily.

Geography/IT
★ Children design an advertising leaflet to encourage visitors to visit a place in their town that they believe needs more support.

DT
★ Children work in small groups to create suitable packaging in which to sell goods such as a new cereal or chocolate bar. They consider lettering, use of colour and slogans.

Teacher's notes

Use the **Challenge Cards** (Resource Sheet 50) to extend the unit.

Activity Sheet 1

Begin with a discussion about why persuasion is important. Ask children to think of something they would like to persuade their parents to do e.g. buy them a pet, a computer game which their parents don't approve of, influence the family choice of holiday. In pairs, children role-play three or four conversations with an adult on one of these topics. They record or note the conversations and make a list of the words and phrases used. Together, record some of these phrases and talk about their usefulness. Provide children with recent newspapers and ask them to find persuasive headlines and stories. From a range of other persuasive materials (letters, brochures, advertisements) ask children with a partner to choose two and record their observations on the activity sheet. Remind them that not all pieces of persuasive text will have all the features.

Activity Sheet 2

Discuss with children the idea of having a school garden in which to grow vegetables. After an initial introduction to the topic, break the class into small groups and ask them to make a list of points which might help them to persuade the head teacher and the school governors that it is a good idea. They note all their ideas, and then organise them into a logical order, with the most powerful arguments first. Also on the sheet they make a list of useful words and phrases, including those which: appeal to logic; appeal to senses; appeal to emotions. Give pairs of children the activity sheet and ask them to draft their persuasive text. Give them time to revise their draft and display the finished texts. Hold a class vote on the most persuasive text, and give a copy of it to the head teacher.

Activity Sheet 3

Using the structure and features developed in activity 2, give children the task of writing a persuasive letter to the local council about something they feel is important to their community – the need for more recreation space, longer opening hours for the library or museum or another issue. Recap on the structure of a persuasion, then give the activity sheet to children in pairs, to use for their draft. After completing their draft, ask them to swap with a partner and review each other's work (possibly using Resource Sheet 30). After the review, children revise their letter and write a finished letter on paper or on the computer. If possible, take the letters to the local council. Children will be encouraged if they receive a response.

Activity Sheet 4

Plan an advertisement for a new sweet or chocolate or a new and amazing skateboard. Recap on the purpose of advertising, and who it is aimed at. Talk about the necessary features: the need to be clear about what the item or service being promoted actually is: an appeal to the consumer's logic and to their emotions; an appeal to their senses; a command to buy the product or use the service plus something eye catching in the form of a photo, illustration, graph or other form of visual. Provide children with the activity sheet for them to create a selling pitch for this exciting new product. Remind them to use positive language, technical jargon, bias, emotion, commands … If time permits give them the opportunity to create a visual representation of their advertisement.

Activity Sheet 5

Discuss with the children the '3 Rs – Reduce, Reuse and Recycle'. Tell them that they are going to create PowerPoint presentations to display in the school reception area to persuade people of the importance of the 3 Rs. Divide children into groups and give them the activity sheet to record important messages for the presentation, from their research. Display the questions on Resource Sheet 49; are there other questions which should be considered? After a period of time, the groups reform, discuss all the suggestions and decide what their message is going to be. They should use the persuasion structure (display the frame from activity 2): statement of opinion; reasons (in logical order); conclusion and call to action. Part of the group can work on the draft text while the rest of the group can source any graphics or photos they want to use. Give each group time to complete their presentation.

Activity Sheet 6

Ask the children to think of instances when a different text would be needed to persuade different groups of people. Give the children a topic such as 'Skateboard Safety'. How would you write to persuade children, adults, manufacturers of skateboard equipment and local councils about the importance of safety? Give the activity sheet to pairs of children and ask them to research and discuss a brochure or poster advertising a holiday in Egypt; they should target either adults or children. Make sure both target audiences are covered. Revise with the children what makes a persuasion. Discuss with them the need to research the necessary information and then find an effective way of presenting it. They can begin by researching Egypt and making notes of the details on the activity sheet. They should look for activities which will appeal to children (staying in a hotel with a pool and short trips) or adults (longer trips with guides). When they have drafted their brochures, suggest they use a design package on the computer to create an integrated text. (*Visit Egypt*, by Jill Laidlaw may help.)

Activity Sheet 7

Ask the children to think about why they would be a good addition to the school council. Talk about the role of the school council and the kind of qualities it looks for in its members. Together make a list of these attributes. Ask children to work with a partner first to discuss why they would make a good member of the school council. Ask them to explain in a leaflet to be distributed throughout the school why they would be the ideal choice. Remind them to include emotional language, possible bias, plenty of adjectives and commands.

REFLECTION & FEEDBACK suggestions

Look back at one of the activities, and review the persuasive text or presentation created. Is there a way to evaluate its impact, in the school or in the community?

Persuasive posters

Talk about the variety of posters around school. Send a couple of children out with a camera to take photos of any examples they find in and around the school buildings and playground to share with the class. Discuss use of positive language, eye catching illustration, commands, slogans and so on.

Slogans

Talk to the children about branding. Ask them to recall different food/drink/ sportswear/fast food chains which rely heavily on associating their product with a slogan or motif. See if the children can draw any motifs from memory.

Support it

Photocopy the statements on Resource Sheet 51 and cut them out. In pairs, children select a card and try to persuade a partner of the points of view on the card, regardless of their own opinion.

What's inside?

Look at and discuss the way in which goods are packaged. Talk about the persuasive effects of these on consumer spending. Look at the way in which toys are packaged. Bring in packaging from a range of toys. Study how the toy is being promoted on the packet. Look at the use of colour, lettering, catch phrase or slogan and educational claims. Do the children think the packaging is successful in helping to sell the toy? If so, why?

An advert for ...?

Ask the children to talk about their favourite adverts from television or radio. Can they identify what the advert is promoting and how the advert is persuading consumers to buy? Encourage them to recollect any jingle or slogan, and whether they think the advert is successful. List successful and unsuccessful adverts on the board with reasons. Show magazine adverts with the product name blocked out and ask children to guess what they are advertising.

What makes a persuasion?

Learning Objective: To understand the structure and features of a persuasion.

Name _____ **Date** _____

Compare the two different texts which are trying to persuade others.

	Text 1	Text 2
Is there an opening statement, with background information?		
Is there a statement of opinion?		
Are there points supported by evidence?		
Are there carefully selected facts?		
Is there a concluding statement?		
Is there an appeal to: ● logic? ● senses? ● emotions?		
Devices: ● Bias ● Half-truths ● Ambiguities ● Rhetorical questions ● Emotive language		
Facts		
Opinions		
What was the writer's purpose?		
Did it achieve the purpose?		

Plan a persuasion

Learning Objective: To plan a persuasive text using a writing frame.

Name _____ **Date** _____

Use the facts and opinions you have discussed with your group to draft a persuasive text.

Heading
Statement of opinion

| **Reasons** Connect your reasons using logical connectives:

As
If … then
As a result
So
Because
Therefore | |

Conclusion Including action required

Review your draft, make changes and write your finished text on the computer or in your book.

Activity Sheet 3
A persuasive letter

Learning Objective: To draft and write a persuasive letter.

Name _____ Date _____

Think carefully about the points you want to make before you draft your letter.

(your address)

(date)

(recipient's address)

(greeting)

Purpose and opinion		
Reasons		
Conclusion and action		

(sign off)

Buy this product

Learning Objective: To use descriptive and persuasive language to promote goods.

Name _____ **Date** _____

Write down all the words and phrases which will help you sell the product. Think of a name and a slogan which will appeal to children.

Name:

Target audience:

Appeal to logic:

Appeal to senses:

Appeal to emotions:

Slogan:

The 3 Rs

Learning Objective: To research and plan a PowerPoint slide show for the school.

Name _____ **Date** _____

Write down your ideas for important messages to include in your presentation, include your ideas for visuals with each message.

Statement of opinion	**Call to action**	

Visit Egypt

Learning Objective: To research and plan a holiday brochure for different audiences.

Name _____ **Date** _____

Destination: Egypt	**Travel Itinerary:**
Transport to Egypt:	Day 1
Transport within Egypt:	Day 2
Accommodation:	Day 3
Top things to see:	Day 4
Top things to do:	Day 5
	Day 6
	Day 7

Vote for me!

Learning Objective: To use positive, persuasive techniques through language and illustration.

Name _____ **Date** _____

Work on your draft below. Consult with your writing partner afterwards to check your work and swap ideas. Include photos or pictures in your finished work.

the candidate
with vision

I would make a good member of the School Council because: (statement of opinion)

_____

_____

_____

_____

All about me and why I am the best candidate.
(reasons, with evidence from background)

_____

_____

_____

If I am elected, I will:

_____

_____

_____

BIOGRAPHY AND AUTOBIOGRAPHY

Purpose	to describe the events in the life, or part of the life, of the subject or self
Structure	opening (orientation); sequence of events, usually in chronological order with important achievements highlighted; closing statement, often most important achievement or legacy
Language features	past tense verbs; third person (biography) or first person (autobiography); temporal or time connectives; evaluative or personal statements (opinions)
Visual features	photographs and illustrations; timelines
Examples	books; newspaper, magazine and internet articles; sports journals; obituaries

Cross-curricular suggestions

History
★ Children undertake research and write a biography of famous or ordinary people from the period of history being studied. They present these in a variety of forms – diaries, storyboards or even cartoons.

ICT
★ Children use the internet to aid research on the subject of biographies.

ICT and Art
★ Create 'Bio Cards' using an art package. Ask children to research and write text for a set of 'Author Cards' or 'Actor Cards' which can be swapped at school.

Teacher's notes

Use the **Challenge Cards** (Resource Sheet 54) to extend the unit.

Activity Sheet 1

Provide a range of autobiographies for children to read and discuss with each other. They then tell each other 'What I know' after reading one of the titles. Discuss the structure of autobiographies; they are recounts told by the author about their own life. Ask children to think about their own lives. If they were going to write their own autobiography what would they include? Make a list of important questions they should think about e.g. What were the key events in your life? How did you feel? What did you think? Who are the important people in your life? Why are they important? What do you share? Leave these questions on display to reference later. Ask some specific questions to prompt memories e.g. What was the funniest time? What is your oldest memory? Who has been your best friend? Do you have a special place? Give each child a copy of the activity sheet and ask them to complete the timeline with significant dates, then write or draw about four important events. Remind them to use rich and vivid descriptions of people and places, to bring the autobiography alive for the reader, and to use 'I' throughout the text. Encourage children to bring in photos which they can arrange in a timeline, and add captions. Write an opening sentence or paragraph together and ask children to write their own in their books, or use Resource Sheet 52. They then write a draft of the most important events and finally a closing statement. Children swap their drafts and review and comment upon each others' work. When children have written a revised piece of text they could 'publish it', make a recording or create a PowerPoint presentation.

Activity Sheet 2

Revisit the structure of the autobiography the children have written. Ask them if they found it easy or difficult to write, and why. Tell them that they are going to research a person from history, and write their autobiography, in role. Ask them what they would need to do first? Research all the information possible, so that they know the details of the subject's life, to recount. In pairs or small groups ask children to choose their subject, then give them the activity sheet for their notes. They could use the library and the internet to research their subject, and make a list of the sources they use. (This is good practice.) When they have completed the notes they could create a timeline for the character, showing the significant events. They can use Resource Sheet 52, their books or the computer to draft the autobiography. Suggest they swap their draft with another group for review, before writing the finished version. Remind them to use rich and vivid descriptions of people and places, to bring the autobiography alive for the reader, and as they are writing in role to use 'I' throughout the text.

Activity Sheet 3

Look with the children at a selection of football/basketball/cricket trading cards. Discuss the fact that these are actually mini biographies of the sports personality, giving quite a lot of information about the person's life. Make a list of the kinds of facts found on this type of card. Give the activity sheet to children in pairs and ask them to choose two sporting personalities to create cards for. Stress that the information is always written in the third person. When they have completed the sheet, ask them to create cards using an art program on the computer and importing a photo from a clip bank.

Activity Sheet 4

Look at some biographies together and make a list of the differences. Invite children to suggest suitable questions that a biographer would need to ask their subject and make a list together. Children then work in pairs to produce their own list of questions. Encourage them to order the questions chronologically instead of randomly. Finally, they take turns asking each other the questions and filling in the questionnaires with their partner's answers. Once completed, individuals can feed back to the class the information found out in a small, informal presentation. Tell children that they are going to research and write a biography. Discuss possible subjects and display photos of possibilities (Resource Sheet 53 has some examples). Ask children to choose one subject and, with a partner, use their questions to research the subject. They will find it useful to make a timeline, and list the important events in their subject's life, in addition to answering their questions. They use the activity sheet to write a first draft of their text. After having their draft reviewed and making their changes, they write their finished text on the computer, print it out and display it for others to read.

Activity Sheet 5

Collect some obituaries from the newspaper and give children time to read some prior to beginning the activity. Discuss the fact that an obituary is really a form of biography, with the same kind of function as a public information board. Review the obituaries you have collected and ask children the difference between them and a biography. One of the main differences is that the contribution the person made to their country or an area of life – the arts, sport etc, – begins the text and personal information about their family etc. is usually at the end of the piece. Often obituaries are prepared some time in advance and updated regularly so that when the person dies the obituary is ready. In pairs, children choose a person, perhaps a famous author or actor, for whom they are going to prepare an obituary. Suggest they research the main facts in the person's life, and remind them to write in the third person.

REFLECTION & FEEDBACK suggestions

Invite children to say whether they found biography or autobiography easiest or most enjoyable to write and why. Ask children to discuss why they think biographies and autobiographies are important? Why do people choose certain episodes and stories to include and not others? What would children miss out of their life story and what do they feel would be interesting for others to read?

GETTING STARTED

A life story

Children work in pairs to make a collage of the life of someone who interests them, using pictures cut out from magazines, papers and from the internet.

Why are they famous?

Ask the children to name some famous people from the past or the present day who interest them. Why are these people famous? What were their achievements? List some of their suggestions on the board. Encourage the class to research all media to compile facts about these people and their lives.

Did you know?

When children have read an autobiography, ask them to compile questions based on the information they have learnt. They can then ask other pupils the questions and discuss the differences and similarities.

Hall of fame

Bring in biographies of famous figures from the past and present day to make a quick classroom display. Be sure to include examples from popular culture e.g. footballers/pop stars/sports and television personalities.

Who is it?

Ask a volunteer to think of a famous figure but not to reveal the name. The class must try to work out the identity of the person using only yes/no questions.

What do we know?

Choose two or three famous people. Display their pictures on the wall. Ask the children to work in pairs to think of questions they would like to put to these people. They can then invent funny or interesting answers.

Activity Sheet 1

Timeline

Learning Objective: To organise biographical facts in chronological order.

Name _____ Date _____

List the significant dates in your life on the timeline. Use the boxes to write about some of the most important events, and why they were important.

Timeline Date (year)	Important events	Why were they important?

Activity Sheet 2
Research

Learning Objective: To research a subject from history to write an autobiography in role.

Name _____ **Date** _____

With your writing partner, research your historical subject and make notes in the boxes. When you have finished your research make a timeline of the important events and use the information you have found to draft the autobiography.

Personal details

Important events

Interesting facts

Name

Achievements

Other notes

Fact file: sporting heroes

Learning Objective: To use facts about someone's life to create a mini biography about that person.

Name _____ **Date** _____

Choose two of your favourite sporting personalities. Using sports magazines, books and the internet, research both personalities and make notes. Provide a picture of each and biographical information. Collaborate with your partner to select only the most important pieces of information for the fact files.

🏆 **Sporting Heroes**

★ _____
★ _____
★ _____
★ _____

🏆 **Sporting Heroes**

★ _____
★ _____
★ _____
★ _____

List your information sources. Record whether they are biographical or autobiographical sources.

_____
_____
_____
_____
_____

Make your cards on the computer and swap them with friends.

Activity Sheet 4
Biography

Learning Objective: To use questions to extract relevant biographical information and to draft a biography from research.

Name _____ **Date** _____

Name:

Orientation:
(Opening statement - birth, family, personal details)

_____
_____
_____
_____
_____
_____
_____
_____

Series of events:
(In chronological order)

_____
_____
_____
_____
_____
_____
_____
_____
_____
_____
_____
_____
_____
_____
_____
_____

Closing statement:
(Comment on important achievements, and why)

_____
_____
_____
_____
_____
_____
_____
_____

Obituary

Learning Objective: To use biographical facts to write an obituary.

Name _____ **Date** _____

Work with a partner and research the life of the person you have chosen to write an obituary for. Make your notes in the boxes. When you have a finished copy, input the text into a newspaper format on the computer, and add a photograph.

OBITUARY

name:

Contribution to society:

_____

_____

_____

_____

_____

_____

_____

_____

_____

_____

_____

The person is survived by

_____

_____

_____

_____

_____

_____

Main events in life:

_____

_____

_____

_____

_____

JOURNALISTIC WRITING

Purpose	to provide an accurate, objective account of observations and information about actual events and people
Structure	most important information at beginning of the piece, less important and background information later and least important information at the end; headlines that arouse interest and give essence of piece; sometimes one-sentence paragraphs; by-line for writer; sometimes date of piece
Language features	clear and concise writing, often to fit a space; past tense; usually third person; direct and reported speech; facts and sometimes opinions
Visual features	photographs; illustrations, maps and diagrams; film footage
Examples	newspapers, magazines, specialised journals, TV, radio, internet articles, pamphlets, periodicals

Cross-curricular suggestions

Art
★ Provide old black and white photographs as inspiration for an imagined news story for children to write about.

History
★ Children go back in time as a journalist to interview a real figure from the period being studied. They write up interview for publication.

Music
★ Look at the way music is used as a background for some news items on television and radio. Using percussion instruments and voice, children invent some jingles to be used in an imaginary radio programme.

Use the **Challenge Cards** (Resource Sheet 59) to extend the unit.

Activity Sheet 1

Display a collection of newspapers and give children time to read and discuss them in groups. Ask each group to look for the three main types of news reports: human interest; news of the day; analytical reports. Review the purpose of newspapers (and other news media): to provide an accurate, objective record of observations and information on real events and real people. How do newspaper reporters get their news? They respond to reports of events and they research articles. In writing or creating a news report there is an initial need to research the event thoroughly; ask children how they think that is done. The ranking of key points, placed in order of importance is often displayed as an inverted pyramid. Highlight the need to be clear and concise to fit a confined space and be understood from one reading. Also, discuss how less important facts at the end can be dropped if space is tight. Give pairs of children the activity sheet and ask them to find two reports (of different types) and use the sheets to review the articles.

Activity Sheet 2

In small groups, show the children a recording of a news programme. Ask them to consider how the programme is structured to maintain interest. Is the order of features significant? Who is the intended audience? What effects do they think time constraints of programme running order have on news presentation? i.e. to shorten some stories and simply leave others out. Then focus on a couple of individual news reports. Do they differ significantly from the presentation of articles in other forms i.e. papers, radio? Re-watch the video news extracts and give children a copy of the activity sheet on which to make notes about their observations of the structure of each piece of news. Review their findings and get feedback in a class discussion.

Activity Sheet 3

Listen to a radio news programme. Discuss the ways in which it differs from a television news programme. Who is the target audience? Give groups of children a recording of half a dozen radio news reports. Ask them to listen for the main points of the broadcast (are the 5 Ws used?), listen to the language used, the structure and the style. Using the activity sheet, children make notes about the structure of the news reports. How are these notes different from those they took while watching the television news report? Find a recent news item for which you can get both a television and a radio report. Ask the groups to watch and listen to both reports and make a list of the similarities and differences, they can use Resource Sheet 55.

Activity Sheet 4

Discuss the importance of a good headline, in the case of newspapers, or introduction to the report in the case of radio and television. Begin by looking at some examples taken from real news stories, talk about purpose i.e. eye-catching/ funny/sombre/scathing. As a class, make a collection of newspaper headlines or use those on Resource Sheet 56. Working with a partner, children discuss possible stories behind each headline. They make a list of the key information to include in their report – remind them to write the information in order of importance. Then ask them to think about presenting the report on radio or television. Give them time to role-play the scene, then write an introduction for each medium. If time permits, record these introductions in both media and display them beside the headlines. Discuss the 'trailers' for important news reports which are run before the news itself on both radio and television. Can children write an effective trailer for their news report? In a plenary share some of the summaries, the radio and television introductions and trailers. Did people who chose the same headline come up with a similar story? Were the trailers exciting enough to convince others to watch or listen to the report later?

Activity Sheet 5

Use the role-play scenario on Resource Sheet 57 or use one children have agreed to. Give groups time to role-play the scenario, and interrogate all of the protagonists for a news report. It may be useful for the groups to change roles so that they are able to think about the events from different points of view. Invite them to produce interviews for a news article and use the activity sheet to make notes for the news article to follow. Children might want to review reporters asking questions on television reports, to help them in the role of reporter. Remind them of the five fundamental questions and to make their notes in the first person in the role of the actual witness. The groups should interview all of the witnesses even if they decide to only use one interview in the report. Share examples of the interviews by asking the children to role-play them for the class.

Activity Sheet 6

Using the interviews and the other notes they have made during the role-play activity, ask children to draft a report. The report can be in any media, although newspaper reports are often a good place to start, with reports in other media following after the news report has been written. Groups can prepare and draft a joint report or make a number of reports by individuals and pairs which they then review and pull together into one after the drafting stage. Remind children of the inverted pyramid, and the importance of beginning with the most important information. More able children could create their report in a given space, i.e. making it shorter or longer. When they have finished their drafts, ask them to swap and have them reviewed. Once changes have been made, the reports can be created using the computer.

Activity Sheet 7

Review some of the human interest stories children have read or seen. Tell them that they are going to create a human interest report for radio or television. They can choose a recent story, or use one of the photos on Resource Sheet 58 as a source. Give them the activity sheet and ask them to make notes for the report. They should role-play interviews with those involved and those who witnessed the event and record interviews or take digital photos for the report. Once the groups have made their notes, they script the report, review and revise it before recording or filming it. When the reports are finished, email them to another school and ask for their feedback.

REFLECTION & FEEDBACK suggestions

Ask children if they watched or read news reports before they began these activities. Will that change now? Are they more interested in the making of news stories now? Which form of news report do they prefer – newspapers, radio or television? Do they think it is easier or more difficult to make reports on radio without the use of pictures of film? Which of the media do they think provides the best news reports?

GETTING STARTED

The 5 Ws

Give pairs of children a newspaper to look through to choose a selection of articles. Ask them to analyse each article to check for inclusion of the 5 Ws – who, what, where, when, why. Share some of their findings with the class.

Match it

Take a range of articles from print media. Cut the headlines from the articles. Give groups of children both the articles and the headlines; can they match them?

Are they all covered?

Watch and re-watch a video news extract. While watching, invite the children to take notes on the 5 W questions.

Radio or television

Introduce other forms of journalistic writing found e.g. on television and radio programmes and the internet through listening to/watching a few example programmes. Discuss the structure and content of this type of writing. Talk about target audience. Discuss whether television or radio has more impact due to techniques such as appealing directly to the audience, frequent updates of news, ability to roll out breaking news, more informal style.

Role-play

Divide the children into groups. Give each group a copy of a different news report. Ask each group to explore the incident through role-play and drama, some children playing eyewitnesses, someone interviewing. The interviewer can ask questions based on the 5 Ws, the interviewees can improvise their answers based on knowledge of the situation gleaned from the news report. Ask for volunteers to perform their drama to the rest of the class.

Same or different

Provide a variety of types of news coverage for the same story. Ask the children to work in groups and consider which reports and which media are the most engaging. Can they articulate why? Ask groups to consider the different methods used by different media and what impact or effect these have. Share the findings of the groups.

Activity Sheet 1
Read all about it!!

Learning Objective: To understand the structure and layout of a newspaper report.

Name _____ Date _____

	Examples from piece	My thoughts/comments
Headline does it *sell* the piece?		
Type of article human interest; news of the day; analytical report		
Purpose of article		
Order of key information information in order of importance		
Uses the 5 Ws who, where, what, when, why		
Facts or opinion?		
Style of language concise; speech – direct/ reported; 3rd person		
Source for piece primary or secondary?		
Interesting / Engaging?		

Analyse a television news programme

Learning Objective: To understand some key features of the way a television news programme is structured and presented.

Name _____ Date _____

	Examples from piece	My thoughts/comments
Programme and presenter		
Introduction to piece *does it create interest?*		
Type of piece *human interest; news of the day; analytical report*		
Purpose of piece		
Order of key information *information in order of importance*		
Uses the 5 Ws *who, where, what, when, why*		
Presenter's pitch, tone, pace of speech		
Style of speech *fact or opinion; Standard English or slang; expression of emotion?*		
Visual support *film of event; witnesses; graphics*		
Interesting / Engaging?		

Take note! Analyse a radio news programme

Learning Objective: To listen to an aural news report and take effective notes for a specific purpose.

Name _____ Date _____

	Examples from piece	My thoughts/comments
Programme and presenter		
Introduction to piece *does it create interest?*		
Type of piece *human interest; news of the day; analytical report*		
Purpose of piece		
Order of key information *information in orderof importance*		
Uses the 5 Ws *who, where, what, when, why*		
Presenter's pitch, tone, pace of speech		
Style of talk *fact or opinion; Standard English or slang; expression of emotion?*		
Aural support *witnesses; reporter; sounds or sound effects*		
Interesting / Engaging?		

Headlines

Learning Objective: To understand that the headline of a piece must encapsulate the mood and content of that piece.

Name _____ **Date** _____

Choose a headline and write some of the key information you think would appear in the article or piece.

Headline:		
Key information of article:		
If the article was reported on the radio or television news, how would the piece be introduced?	Radio:	Television:
If there was a 'trailer' for the piece on radio or television, what would the trailer say?	Radio:	Television:

Activity Sheet 5
Write an interview

Learning Objective: To use discussion and drama techniques to explore a particular event, incident or situation and its protagonists.

Name _____ **Date** _____

You are a reporter who has gone to interview a witness to a news event. Make your notes here.

Witness's name: _____

About the witness: _____

_____

_____

Summary of fact _____

_____

_____

Remember to include: _____

Who _____

When _____

Where _____

Why _____

What _____

What else the witness saw or heard. _____

_____

How the witness felt _____

_____

What would be a good headline? _____

_____

_____

_____

Activity Sheet 6
News report

Learning Objective: To write an effective news report in journalistic style.

Name _____ Date _____

Look back at the notes you made when you interviewed the witness to the news event. Use those notes to draft your story. Remember to use clear and concise language.

Headline	
Lead paragraph about main event. *Who, what, when and where.*	
Next important information – background. *Why and how.*	
Less important information	
Least important information.	

Report on human interest story

Learning Objective: To report on a human interest event, selecting language and content to suit audience and purpose.

Name _____ Date _____

Collaborate with your group to organise the draft ideas for your radio or television report.

Story:

Who?

What?

Where?

When?

Why?

Summary of the event:

What the protagonists and witnesses said:

Good introduction:

Key information in order of delivery:

Interviews to use:

Other visual or aural information to use in the piece:

aRGUMENT

Purpose	to argue a case for or against an opinion, using evidence to support it
Structure	opening statement of opinion or point of view; arguments in support of the opinion, from strongest to weakest argument; facts in support of the opinion; conclusion with reinforcement of opinion and sometimes a recommendation
Language features	action verbs; emotive words and phrases; present tense; technical terms and specialist language; time and cause/effect connectives; may include quotes
Visual features	photographs; illustrations; charts and graphs
Examples	letters; newspaper and magazine editorials and articles; leaflets and posters; radio and television editorials and programmes

Cross-curricular suggestions

Geography
★ Children argue a case for the preservation of an area of natural beauty or geographic importance which is under threat.

PSHE
★ Children present an argument for the merits of recycling glass, paper and aluminium.

History
★ Children argue the case for and against some of the great historical debates, such as Richard III killed the 'princes in the tower' or those involved in the opening of King Tutankhamun's tomb were cursed and they all died early.

Teacher's notes

Use the **Challenge Cards** (Resource Sheet 61) to extend the unit.

Activity Sheet 1

Begin the session by asking children how they might argue for something e.g. more computer time in the classroom. Ask them to discuss it with a partner, and then write their points on the board. Were all the points in favour of the opinion, or were there 'for' and 'against'? Tell children that when presenting an argument in favour of an opinion or point of view it is useful to have considered the other point of view, so that you can counter it. Together write some issues on the board such as 'Is having a school uniform a good thing? Should the school have a garden to grow vegetables? Should there be water coolers in every classroom?' Give pairs of children a copy of the activity sheet and ask them to choose an issue. They plan an argument with their partner making notes of the arguments for and against. Soundings could be taken from other students and adults in the school, then the children decide on their own concluding point of view based on the evidence.

Activity Sheet 2

Discuss with children a range of community and global issues for them to discuss, such as: *Cars should not be allowed in the town centre. All zoos should be banned. Wearing of animal furs should be banned. Limited whale hunting should be allowed.* Make a list on the board and ask children in groups to choose one of the issues to discuss further. Display the model text on Resource Sheet 60. Read the text together and add the structure and language features captions (at the bottom of the page) to it. Discuss the argument structure: Give an opening statement to introduce the topic; give arguments in support of your opinion; give your strongest point first; give evidence for your arguments; conclude with a statement and a call to action. Look for language features such as: action verbs; time connections; cause/effect connections, emotive words and phrases; present tense; technical terms and specialist language. Ask the children to think of other words and phrases which could be used to improve the text. Give the activity sheet to pairs of children and ask them to choose one of the issues discussed earlier and make notes for their argument. Once they have researched and made their points, they write a draft of their argument. Suggest that they swap drafts with someone and review each other's work. (Resource Sheet 30 can be used.) They make alterations to their draft using the 'Proofreading' General Reference Sheet and write (or type) a polished version of their argument.

Activity Sheet 3

Explore with children different graphic organisers they can use to martial the points for their arguments, e.g. a logic chain, a flow chart, a Venn diagram. Ask children to choose another issue, for instance: *Tourism is a good thing. Schools should devote one afternoon per week to sport. A wind farm should not to be built near the school. Children should be made to study a Martial Art. Why we should use more electric cars rather than diesel or petrol vehicles.* Give children the activity sheet and ask them to research the arguments for and against their chosen issue. Ask them to look for evidence for each of their arguments, and to make a list of source material on the back of the sheet. When they have completed their sheets, put them into groups of four and ask two to take one side of the argument and two to take the other side. Give them five minutes to think about their own arguments, then ask them to role-play their arguments in a discussion. The discussions could be recorded, or some groups could be asked to role-play for the class. In a plenary, discuss the arguments used, and their effectiveness.

Activity Sheet 4

Discuss the issue of schools selling off their playing fields in order to make money. Ask for views and have an open discussion of the arguments for and against this. Write up pros and cons and appropriate vocabulary on the board. Give the activity sheet to pairs of children and ask them to discuss and then lay out their arguments against (or for) this proposal for their school. The sheet can be used to make notes. When they have made their notes and drafted their arguments they either use their arguments to write a letter which could be sent to the council (using the argument structure in their letter) or create a PowerPoint presentation which could be shown to the school council. Remind them that it will help their argument if they can provide a sensible alternative solution and that they should have a clear and achievable call to action.

Activity Sheet 5

Give children the opportunity to listen to the arguments for and against an issue, either by listening to a radio debate, watching one on television or listening to a discussion by class members. Give them the activity sheet on which to make notes as they listen. Ask them to listen carefully as the two groups present their arguments to see if they are clear about the arguments being put forward and the evidence being provided. Ask for their opinions at the end of the discussion or programme; have they changed their mind about the issue?

REFLECTION & FEEDBACK suggestions

Send some of the children into other classrooms to present one of the arguments prepared by groups. Take a vote from the other classes after they have heard the arguments. Discuss the results afterwards.

Getting Started

Weekend work

Children work in small groups to collaborate on the argument that all 13-year-olds should do a small amount of paid work at the weekends. Ask them to make a list of their arguments as to why this would be a good thing, with a view to presenting their ideas to the class. Remind them they must elaborate on each argument on their list.

After these have been heard, ask if anyone can come up with arguments against this.

Influencing ads

Hold a class discussion on whether advertising aimed at children should be allowed during the breaks in children's television programmes. Divide the class into two; one half arguing for, and the other half against. List their ideas on the board. Take a vote on the issue at the end.

Persuasive words

Read through some examples of letters to the editor taken from local newspapers. Invite the class to come up with imagined details about the person who wrote the letters. On a large piece of card, list useful vocabulary found in the letters e.g. I think, some people think, people claim, it is said that, on the other hand, in my opinion, it seems that, it is the case that, firstly, secondly, finally, it is important that, therefore, as a result …
and so on.

Reporter in the street

Using the statements on Resource Sheet 62, children take on the roles. The reporter in each instance interviews the people in other roles and asks for their response to the statement.

Role-play

Children work in pairs to role-play an argument between a child and a parent as to whether that child should be allowed to have a pet. Invite volunteers to present their role-play to the class. Highlight the features of an argument i.e. introduction of the issue, arguments for and against with supporting evidence and elaboration, reinforcement of the initial point of view.

Arguments for

Activity Sheet 3

For and against

Learning Objective: To summarise different sides of an argument.

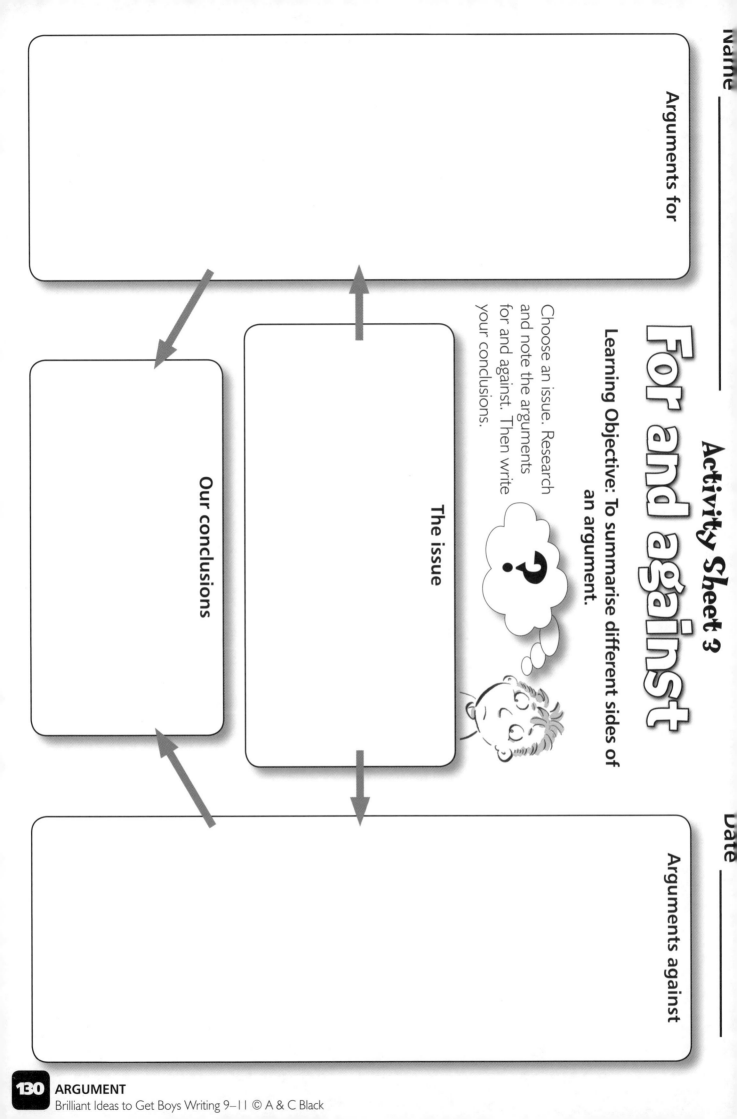

Choose an issue. Research and note the arguments for and against. Then write your conclusions.

The issue

Our conclusions

Arguments against

Activity Sheet 2
Plan an argument

Learning Objective: To plan an argument and provide evidence.

Name _____ Date _____

Choose an issue, research and note the arguments for and against. Then write your conclusions.

The issue:

Opening statement:

include your opinion, emotional statement and background

Argument 1:

Evidence/elaboration:

Argument 2:

Evidence/elaboration:

Argument 3:

Evidence/elaboration:

Helpful vocabulary
firstly; if; then; as a result; because; in addition; so; this will cause; one can see; it is clear; therefore; for these occasions

For and against

Learning Objective: To summarise fairly competing views and signal personal opinion.

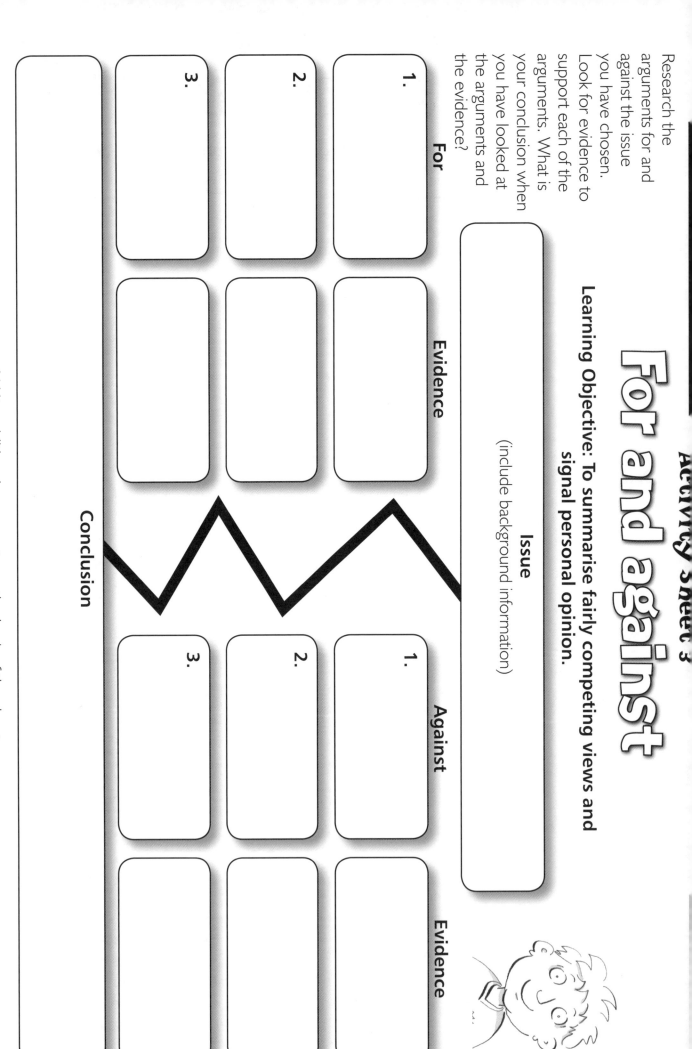

Research the arguments for and against the issue you have chosen. Look for evidence to support each of the arguments. What is your conclusion when you have looked at the arguments and the evidence?

Issue
(include background information)

For

1.

2.

3.

Evidence

Against

1.

2.

3.

Evidence

Conclusion

Write additional arguments on the back of the sheet.

Save our playground!

Learning Objective: To present persuasive evidence and signal personal opinion clearly.

Name _____ **Date** _____

Work with a partner. Imagine you have just found out that your local council is considering selling the school playgrounds and fields to provide a new car park for the town. You are both heavily opposed to this idea.

Remember to provide evidence for your arguments.

Our point of view

Argument 1

Make sure your arguments are in a logical order.

Argument 2

Argument 3

Argument 4

What do you think?

Learning Objective: To listen to two sides of an argument being presented and to reach a reasoned personal conclusion.

Name _____ Date _____

Listen to the arguments for and against the issue. Make notes while you listen. Discuss your thoughts with a partner when both sides have been presented, then add your opinion to the sheet.

One side of the arguments says
They claim that
1.
2.
They also say that
3.
4.
The other side of the argument says
They claim that
1.
2.
They also say that
3.
4.
After listening to both sides of the argument, I think
because

FORMAL AND INFORMAL WRITING

Purpose	to give and receive information in a formal way; may include instruction, explanation, report, persuasion or a combination of non-fiction forms
Structure	appropriate to task and audience
Language features	precise, accurate, clear and concise language; usually present tense; passive verbs; formal language;
Visual features	illustrations and photos; maps, charts and diagrams; film and video
Examples	letters; brochures; posters; consumer information; advertisements; guides

Cross-curricular suggestions

ICT
★ Children use word processing packages to produce formal communications for the classroom.

Science
★ Children produce a poster warning the public of the dangers of smoking.

History
★ Children choose a figure from the topic being studied and write a formal letter as that character e.g. Henry VII; Anne Boleyn; A Roman Senator; Cleopatra ...

Literacy
★ Children produce an advertisement or letter to parents outlining a school play or special event.

Teacher's notes

Activity Sheet 1

Ask children to give some examples of formal and informal speech e.g. 'There is no possibility of that' (formal); 'No chance' (informal). Challenge one half of the class to think of formal statements and the other half to give an informal equivalent, or visa versa (the second is easier). Then ask children to think of examples of formal writing around the school, and at home. Encourage them to include different non-fiction forms in the list e.g. instructions – for exams, to fill in forms; explanations – in letters, brochures; persuasive writing – in letters, brochures; mixed forms – brochures, guides. Make a list and discuss why they are formal communications; audience, purpose and language can all help with this. Collect a range of formal communications; and display or scan them to make a PowerPoint presentation. Highlight the structure and language features which signal a 'formal' communication on some of the examples, make notes of the verb tenses and the 'formal' words used. Give the activity sheet to pairs of children and ask them to choose three or four communications and complete the sheet. Ask them to look for examples of impersonal voice, imperative words, formal vocabulary, both words and phrases. When they have finished, discuss their answers.

Activity Sheet 2

Begin by discussing the conventions of formal letter writing. Discuss examples of formal/impersonal words and phrases. Ask children to give you salutations and signing off for formal letters. If you have made a collection of formal letters (Getting Started), display some of these letters and discuss them together. Children should notice the two types of sign off – yours faithfully and yours sincerely. Ask if anyone can guess what the difference is from looking at the letters, (yours sincerely is used when you know the name of the recipient). In pairs, children choose one of the letter scenarios on Resource Sheet 63 and discuss the purpose of the letter and the audience. They then use the activity sheet to write a draft of their letter. If necessary, remind them where to place their address, recipient's address, date, body of letter, sign off and signature. When they have finished give them time to discuss with a writing partner, to edit and improve the letter before writing or typing a finished version.

Activity Sheet 3

Make a collection of guides and brochures detailing buildings and sites local to the school which attract visitors. Discuss with the children the purpose and the audience for each of these. Then ask the children, in pairs, to discuss an example together and feed back their thoughts on the material to the class. Is the communication formal or informal? How do they know that? What else can they tell you about the example? Encourage them to talk about the layout and the visual texts as well as the content. Agree as a class on a local venue – house, building, outdoor space – which will be the subject of their brochure. Firstly decide what the purpose of the brochure will be and who the audience will be. Divide the class into groups and give them copies of the activity sheet on which to collect their information. Remind children to work as a team and to allocate jobs to members of the team, rather than all doing everything. The information gathered in this activity will be used in the next activity, when they plan and create a brochure for the subject.

Activity Sheet 4

Give the activity sheet to groups and ask them to use the brochure layout to plan the placement of text, photos, maps and illustrations. It may be possible to put the brochure template onto the computer, in which case children could use this to plan their layout. Remind them that they should not accept the first draft they make; it might be possible to ask pairs within the group to create layouts, then bring them together and discuss the pros and cons of each, before coming to a consensus. Remind children that this is how a magazine would work – people in different roles bring their ideas to an editorial meeting, where they are all discussed, altered and improved. Once they have agreed the layout they want to use, the group should break up into the roles they had agreed earlier; so that everyone is working on a draft of their task – maps, illustrations, photos, text boxes, copy etc. The drafts can be reviewed before they are input into the program, or when the first draft of the whole brochure is complete. However they do need to edit, proofread and review the draft, before moving to a finished brochure.

Activity Sheet 5

If possible obtain a copy of an audio guide from a museum, gallery or a local walk. Ask children to think about the format – the speaker stops at selected sites, and the audio guide provides information about the picture, the display or the place. There are often some rehearsed speeches between stops. Give children the opportunity to listen and then to role-play a short guide to a partner, perhaps of one or two places within the classroom or in the immediate vicinity. Tell children that they are going to create an audio tour of the school for visitors, new pupils or prospective parents. Give them a copy of the activity sheet and, in pairs, they go out and decide which parts of the school will be important to include in their tour and why. Firstly they should agree with their partner the purpose of the tour and the audience. It may be important to limit the number of 'stops' on the tour, otherwise children will not finish. Remind them to think about where they would begin and what they would say at the beginning of the tour. They will use this information in the next activity.

Activity Sheet 6

Using the information they agreed in the last activity, children now use that outline information to construct their audio text. Give the pairs the activity sheet, but explain that they will have to use additional paper to write the text for each 'stop'. Remind them to think about the linking speech they will use to move people from one stop to another. They should use the skills they have learned about non-fiction texts in writing their speech, for instance it is important to have an introductory and a concluding paragraph for the tour. They should reflect on the structure of the information text used for each stop. When they have written a first draft, suggest that together they review the draft, cut out superfluous words and phrases, check the language used and edit the text. Once they have done this, they record the text as a draft; so that they can listen to it and check for improvements they might make in their delivery. When they have recorded their finished guide, ask them to swap with another pair.

REFLECTION & FEEDBACK suggestions

Print the brochures and display them in school, or in the local community; ask for feedback from readers. Use the audio guides to take groups of children around the school, and at the end of the tour ask them to rate the tour or give them a questionnaire to answer to evaluate it.

GETTING STARTED

Letters home

Make a collection of formal letters which are written at school. (Ask the school secretary to give you copies of letters to add to the collection.) Display the letters together or paste them into a book. Annotate each letter with a note saying who is the audience for the letter, what its purpose is and why it is a formal letter.

Role-play

Collect formal texts of many types and place them into a box. Ask children to pick one out and then assume the role of the person they think wrote the text. Ask the class if they think the person reading the text was correct.

Shop ads

Talk about the kinds of adverts typically seen on a notice board in a shop. Discuss why a local shop is a good forum for community messages. Are they formal communications? How do you know?

Take note

Using a digital camera, children take photographs of public signs and posters which are formal texts, either in the school, or if the opportunity arises, in the local area. Make a display of the photos, attaching captions to say who each one is aimed at, where it was and what its purpose is.

Too formal

With a partner, children choose a written communication which can be either formal or informal e.g. a party invitation. They create an example of each and make a note of the differences between the two.

Activity Sheet 1

Why formal?

Learning Objective: To investigate the structure and language features of formal communications.

Choose three or four pieces of formal writing with your writing partner. Discuss them together and complete the table.

Text	Purpose	Audience	How I know it is a formal text (examples from the text)

Formal letter

Learning Objective: To use conventions of formal letter writing in the first person.

Name _____ **Date** _____

Choose one of the scenarios for a formal letter. Write your draft on the sheet, check it with your writing partner, correct it and write or type a finished version.

(address)

(date)

(greeting)

(write the events in order they happened)

(details, feelings and opinions)

(close the letter)

(sign off)

Planning the brochure

Learning Objective: To use a graphic organised to plan a text.

Name _____ Date _____

Create a summary of the key features of your brochure. You might want to change some of the box headings or add further boxes to help your planning.

Purpose: **Audience:**

About the subject
Important points about the venue which must be included – when it is open, how much it costs etc.

Text boxes
What facts, statistics or other information would be best in a text box?

Subject of brochure

Where is it?
Is the venue of importance; how will people get there?

Photos
What photos are important to include?

Emotive language
What emotive language will you use to appeal to your readers?

Visual text
What other visuals, such as maps, are important to include?

Title and headings
It is important to have an eye-catching title and strong headings. What type and colours will you use?

Brochure layout

Learning Objective: To plan a text layout, prior to using ICT skills to present text.

Name _____ **Date** _____

Use the sheet to lay out and plan the position of the text, photos, maps and illustrations for your brochure. Remember to use an eye-catching title and bold headlines, as some people may not read the whole brochure. When you have all the text and illustrations, input it into a computer program using the layout plan.

page 2

back

page 1

Facts heading

★ _____
★ _____
★ _____
★ _____
★ _____
★ _____
★ _____
★ _____
★ _____
★ _____
★ _____
★ _____

Title

photo

text

page 3

text

text

photo

photo

photo

Planning the audio guide

Learning Objective: To plan the stages of an audio guide.

Name _____ Date _____

Use the boxes to plan each of the stops of your audio tour of the school. Write in each of the boxes why it is important to include each place to be visited. Add a note to say how you will link to the next stop.

Purpose: Audience:

Remember to add a closing statement, thanking the participants for taking the tour, hoping they have enjoyed it and asking if they have any questions.

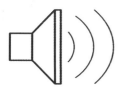
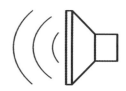

Activity Sheet 6
Audio guide

Learning Objective: To use appropriate language to provide information for an audio guide.

Name _____ **Date** _____

Plan the text for your audio guide in the boxes below. Add additional boxes on the back of the sheet for each of the stops you will make on your tour. Remember your text needs to be clear and concise, informative and interesting. Add the place you will be standing to deliver each part of the guided tour. Record your first draft and ask a partner to listen to it and comment on your content and your delivery. Revise your text and re-record the guide.

Purpose: Audience:

Introduction

How will you greet your participants?

Remember to include the reason for the tour and how long it will take.

Link to 1st stop

1st stop on the tour
Why is this stop important?
What do you need to point out?
Give information clearly and concisely.

Link to next stop

Conclusion
Thank your participants.
Ask them if they have any questions.

General reference sheets

These resources can be used as class discussion prompts by children, as part of activities or as classroom display.

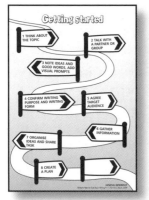

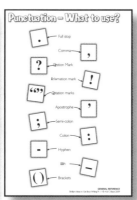

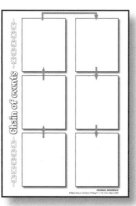

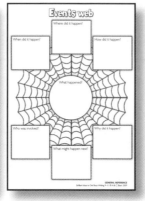

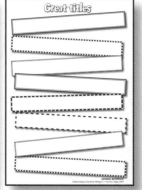

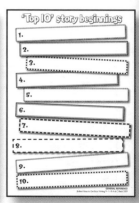